Geolog

C000063509

Somá Menehe
IWM, 25/9/99.

Edited by
J. T. Greensmith

The shell-fountains leap from the swamps,
  and with wild-fire and fume
  The shoulder of the chalkdown convulses.

Edmund Blunden, *Thiepval Wood (1916)*

ISBN 0-900717-59-9

Geology of the Western Front, 1914 - 1918

CONTENTS

PREFACE

The Western Front was the most important theatre of war during the 1914-1918 world conflict. Although this contention has been widely debated, the fact remains that the Somme-Flanders lowland—the centre of British activity—was of great strategic importance, and its possession was a key to the domination of France by Germany and ultimately, of Britain. Fiercely defended, this region of northern France and Belgium is associated with some of the most costly offensives of the war, and every year thousands of visitors make the short journey over (or latterly, under) the English Channel to visit the battlefields.

Although many of the scars of war have been erased forever from the landscape of Artois and Flanders, enough evidence of trenches, dug-outs and the detritus of war remains to remind us of this most monstrous conflict. Over the last ten years or so interest in the Great War has reached an intensity perhaps not seen since the early years of the 1920's, when hundreds of people made pilgrimages to the scenes of conflict in memory of the recent dead. A vast and increasing body of literature is growing to meet the demand; but few if any make more than a passing reference to the importance of terrain (topography and geology) in determining the outcome of the battles in this now long quiet corner of Europe. Today, thousands of tourists and school parties visit the twin meccas of Ypres and the Somme, but how many visitors give more than a passing thought to the terrain: the low hills surrounding Ypres that were so vital to both sides, and so hard fought over; the rolling chalk hills of Artois; the prominent spoil tips of the Lens coalfield; and the distinctive ridges of Vimy and Notre Dame de Lorette?

In reality, the geology and topography of the battlefields of France and Belgium had an important role in determining the character and outcome of many of the most famous battles. In both regions, the occurrence of low (<150 m) hills and ridges provided the focus for many of the most famous attritional battles of the Western Front, as each side fought to gain the strategic advantage provided by the possession of high ground. It is the importance of these and related factors which this field guide is intended to address, by introducing to the visitor some of the aspects of the geology and terrain which made a significant contribution to the outcome of battles on the Western Front. The guide is intended for all people with an interest in the British sector of the Western Front and, although geological terms are included, they are kept to a minimum, and those which are deemed essential are included in a glossary at the end of the guide.

Finally, my interest in the Western Front and the Great War is as old as my interest in geology—too many years for me to care to mention—and combining the two in this guide is a labour of love. If, like me, you had relatives who fought and died in that now distant war, I hope that you will find value in its pages and that it will open your eyes further to the horrors endured eighty or more years ago.

Acknowledgements

I am indebted to my friend and colleague Matthew Bennett for drawing the diagrams in this guide, despite being committed to a whole range of other, more pressing, duties. All the photographs are my own, apart from the wartime images, which are reproduced with the permission of the Trustees of the Imperial War Museum, London. My friend and partner Julie Doyle accompanied me on all of my expeditions to the Western Front, and I thank her for her assistance, suggestions and sound advice. Maggie Magnussen kindly allowed me free access to literature in the Royal Engineers Library at Chatham, and Johan Vanderwalle of Zonnebeke introduced me to the unknown trenches and dug-outs of the Ypres Salient. I would also like to thank Trevor Greensmith and Eric Robinson for their encouragement and advice in bringing this guide to fruition, and finally, my 'guinea pigs'; those seventeen members of the Geologists' Association who accompanied me to the Western Front in July 1998, and who demonstrated that the tours in this guide are both practical and possible. The printing costs of this guide have been assisted by a substantial grant from the Curry Fund of the Geologists' Association.

LIST OF FIGURES

Geology of the Western Front, 1914 - 1918

Geology of the Western Front, 1914 - 1918

GENERAL INFORMATION

Access routes

Northern France and Belgium are easily reached from the southern ports of England to the continental transit destinations of Calais and Boulogne. Both busy French ports were the usual entry and exit points of British and Empire troops to France and Flanders during the war, and several large bases and base hospitals were situated there. For today's traveller, Calais is the easiest option, as it represents the quickest crossing, either via the Channel Tunnel or by the numerous ferries and other sea-going craft. The quickest route southeast to the British sector of the Western Front is via the fast autoroutes. The most useful, and easily available, map for general route finding in the area is the Michelin 1/200,000 map (No 236 in the France series) for the area Nord, Flandres–Artois–Picardy.

The quickest route to Ypres (Ieper), is via the A16 autoroute, travelling eastwards in the direction of Dunkirk (Dunkerque). At *sortie* 28, join the A25 autoroute, travelling south in the direction of Lille. Leave the autoroute at *sortie* 13 (Steenvoorde), following the D948/N38 to Poperinge and then on to Ypres. Access to Arras and the Somme can be gained by rejoining the A25, and travelling to Lille, east of which the main A1 autoroute to Paris can be joined. This toll road provides speedy access to the outskirts of Arras, where it crosses the 1917 battlefield, and to the towns of Bapaume (an objective of the Somme battle) and Peronne, home of a fine new museum *(Le Historial de la Grande Guerre)* dedicated to the Great War. Alternatively, leave the A1 to join the A21 just east of Lens, and follow the ring road to the south, until the N17 road to Arras is reached. This road strikes south southwest to Arras and traverses the Lens coalfield before rising sharply up the scarp of Vimy Ridge and on to Arras. A more direct route from Calais to Arras and the Somme is via the A26 autoroute, in the direction of Reims and St Quentin. This road passes to the south of Vimy Ridge (on its dip slope), past the outskirts of Arras, before joining the A1 to Paris as before. A toll is payable on this route.

Belgian place names

During the Great War, the British Army used almost exclusively the French language spelling of Belgian place names. Today, Flemish names are more commonly applied, so that the familiar Ypres (*'Wipers'* to the British Tommies) is now officially Ieper, and so on. The Commonwealth War Graves Commission and the majority of contemporary accounts use the French language names, and this practice is also followed here, although where appropriate the modern Flemish equivalent is given in parentheses alongside it. All relevant Michelin route maps also carry the bilingual spelling of place names.

Geology of the Western Front, 1914 - 1918

Accommodation

Accommodation is available in all towns in the region although, perhaps surprisingly, there is relatively little choice in and around the Somme battlefield area. In Belgium, there are good hotels in Poperinge and Ypres, and details of accommodation can be obtained direct from the tourist information office (Stadhuis, Grote Markt 34, B-8900 Ieper, Belgium; telephone from the UK 00 32 57 20 07 24). General information for travellers can also be obtained from the Belgian Tourist Office in London (29 Princes Street, London W1R 7RG; telephone 0171 629 0230). Similarly, information on tourism in France can be obtained in London from the French Tourist Office (178, Piccadilly, London W1V 0AL; telephone 0171 493 6594); while advice about hotels can be gleaned from local tourist offices. Arras is a large, pleasant town with several hotels; the local tourist office is in the Hôtel de Ville (Place des Héros; telephone 00 33 3 21 51 26 95). Albert is smaller, and perhaps less pleasant, but is no less interesting because of its strong association with the Great War. It's tourist office is in the rue Gambetta (telephone from the UK 00 33 3 22 75 16 42)

Battlefield debris

The battlefields of the Great War still yield an 'iron harvest' of dangerous debris which includes, in my own personal experience: live rounds; live grenades; live artillery shells (so-called 'duds') of all calibres; live and potentially leaking gas shells; live and extremely volatile 'Stokes' mortar shells; aerial bombs (Figure 1). These dangerous and unstable munitions are regularly ploughed up by the farmers who work the rich soils of Flanders and Artois and are left at suitable points at field boundaries and road intersections for collection by the authorities. These munitions still regularly claim the lives of unwary people every year and although it is

Figure 1. The 'iron harvest'; shells and bullets on the Western Front in 1998.

generally safe to photograph them, please be aware that it would be most unwise to touch or remove such items. Other debris, such as barbed wire, shrapnel balls, and so on also carry some risk from tetanus, if handled, and should be left well alone.

War cemeteries

A striking aspect of the battlefields of France and Belgium is the dense concentration of war cemeteries, often marking the position of old front lines otherwise long erased from the landscape. Each cemetery was designed by famous architects such as Blomfeld, Baker or Lutyens, and was meant to represent an English country garden. They are immaculately cared for by the Commonwealth War Graves Commission (CWGC). A decision was taken by the British authorities early in the war that there should be no repatriation of soldiers who died, and that they should be buried as close as possible to the site of the action in which they were killed. This applied to all ranks and it is possible to see a Lieutenant General buried close to a Private soldier, as no grave is grouped by rank or other distinction. Each grave is marked by a headstone of (usually) Portland Stone, although in recent years Botticino Limestone from Italy has been used, which is inscribed with name and rank, date of death, an appropriate religious symbol and a regimental badge. Unknown soldiers also have individual headstones, which carry the words (chosen by Kipling): '*An unknown soldier of the Great War. Known unto God*'. For those soldiers who have no known grave, a number of large memorials to the missing were erected after the war; the Menin Gate in Ypres and the Thiepval Memorial on the Somme are two striking examples.

The Commonwealth War Graves Commission will operate a search, free of charge, for the grave or site of commemoration of relatives who were killed in the war, although a small charge is usually made where the casualty is not a relative. Further details can be obtained from the CWGC head office in Marlow (2 Marlow Road, Maidenhead, SL6 7DX, telephone 01628 34221), or regional offices in Ieper (82 Elverdingestraat, Ieper; from the UK 00 32 57 20 01 81) and at Beaurains in the outskirts of Arras (rue Angele Richard, 62217 Beaurains; from the UK 00 33 3 21 71 03 24). In addition, the CWGC also supply 1/200,000 scale Michelin road maps with the location of cemeteries in the whole of northern France and Belgium, which are very useful.

In general it is possible to recognise at least three types of cemetery in France and Belgium: (1) small, battlefield cemeteries which have relatively few graves, often from a single regiment and often resulting from a single action. These usually denote battlefield grave sites, the casualties having been buried in trenches or shell holes by their comrades. A classic example is the Devonshire Cemetery near Mametz on the Somme, in which all the graves are of men from the Devonshire Regiment killed on the first day of the battle and buried in a front line trench. This

Geology of the Western Front, 1914 - 1918

trench continues beyond the boundaries of the cemetery into Mansell Copse beyond. (2) Larger cemeteries by the side of roads or rail junctions which are often the sites of Casualty Clearing Stations. To such places, badly wounded soldiers were evacuated out of the battle zone, and those who died were buried on the spot. German prisoners who suffered the same fate were also buried alongside their former enemies, and are marked by their own distinctive headstones. (3) Large cemeteries which started life as one of the other two types, but which were added to after the war by concentration of smaller battlefield cemetery sites. For the most part, French and German cemetery sites are examples of large concentration cemeteries, and there are fewer to be encountered in the region. Today, the remains of soldiers from both sides are still being uncovered and are buried in so-called 'open' cemeteries.

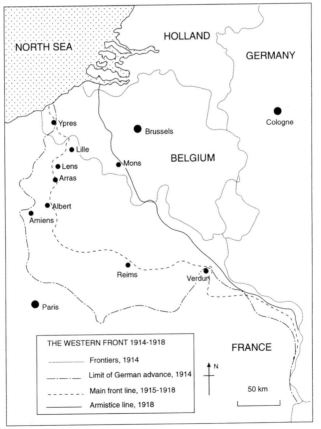

Figure 2. The Western Front, 1914-1918.

THE GREAT WAR ON THE WESTERN FRONT

Background to the Great War

The background to the Great War of 1914-1918 is complex, its origins are much debated, and little space can de devoted to exploring them here. What is clear, however, is that local tensions in the Balkans erupted into world war largely because the major European powers were, in effect, 'spoiling for a fight', and there was a sickening inevitability to the outbreak of hostilities in the summer of 1914.

For over eighty years it has been widely agreed that the Great War was mostly fought and won on the battlefields of Europe. There were costly 'sideshows' of course—Gallipoli, Salonika, Mesopotamia (Iraq), Palestine and East Africa are examples—but in reality the war was conducted in Northwestern and Eastern Europe. This was a war on two fronts for the Central Powers of Germany and Austria-Hungary: facing Russia in the east, and France in the west. The Italian Front opened in 1915 and with Italy facing the Austrians this also added to the pressure on the Central Powers.

The problem of a two front war had long exercised the minds of German military strategists, and the Schlieffen Plan of 1905 was intended to provide an answer. It tackled the problem in the west through the delivery of a fast knockout blow to France via Belgium in the west, using rapid transit of troops on the well-developed European railway system. The western allies, France in particular, were to be despatched in the opening months of war in order to leave longer time to deal with the perceived might of the Russian armies (the 'Russian steamroller') in the east. The plan was a failure for a variety of reasons, most of them to do with tactical provision and disposition of troops, and by the end of 1914 the mobile war in the west had degenerated into a static warfare which employed many of the siege tactics of earlier centuries. After early rapid advances, the German forces were checked at the Battle of the Marne in September 1914 and from November 1914 the Western Front became a line of parallel, entrenched defensive positions which extended from the English Channel to the Swiss frontier (Figure 2). Although it was on this front that the war was finally decided in November 1918, it was not until 1918 that major breakthroughs and mobile warfare were attained.

Principles of trench warfare on the Western Front

Trench warfare has a long history which extends back to at least the 17th century when siege operations utilised defensive trenches, saps and mine systems to breach fortress walls. Trench systems were also widely used in the wars of the mid - to late 19th, and early 20th centuries—the Crimea, the American Civil War and the Russo-Japanese War are examples. It is, however, the Great War which is most commonly associated with this type of static warfare.

The Great War on the Western Front

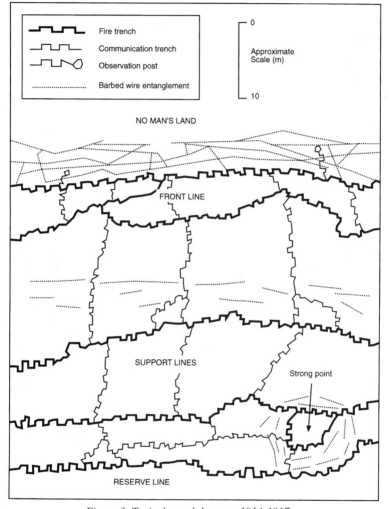

Legend:
- Fire trench
- Communication trench
- Observation post
- Barbed wire entanglement

0 — Approximate Scale (m) — 10

NO MAN'S LAND

FRONT LINE

SUPPORT LINES

Strong point

RESERVE LINE

Figure 3. Typical trench layouts, 1914-1917.

In the Great War, the same basic trench system was employed by all the main protagonists on the Western Front. On both sides, trenches were constructed in roughly parallel rows (Figure 3). Each trench was approximately two metres deep and 0.6 metres wide at the bottom, usually widening to two metres at its top (Figure 4). Raised earth works provided protection at the front (the *'parapet'*) and rear (the *'parados'*) of the trench lip. Trenches were constructed in right-angled zigzag

The Great War on the Western Front

patterns of straight 'bays' designed to prevent enfilading fire (i.e. fire along the length of the trench), and to limit the effect of shell fire and bomb explosions The forward or front line fire trench was equipped with a raised 'firestep' in forward projecting bays, so that troops could stand to see over the top of the trench for offensive action or night sentry duty. Daytime observation was carried out using periscopes. Sandbags, together with timber and wattling anchored with stakes and wires, were used to construct revetments to strengthen and retain the steep sides of trenches. In most trenches, drainage was provided by collecting sumps and using handpumps. Wooden duckboarding was provided to give a reasonable footing to the trench. In some cases, the construction of deep trenches was impossible due to local ground conditions, and in such cases they were replaced by breastworks of sandbags and wood, usually two metres high and up to three metres wide. In others, a series of unconnected forward outposts and concrete emplacements were used instead of a coherent front line.

Figure 4. Preserved trenches at the Hill 62 Trench Museum, Belgium. These trenches are cut in the Paniselian Formation, overlying the Ypres Clay.

The front line trenches of the opposing armies were separated by a belt of contested ground known as 'No Man's Land', usually extensively pitted by shell holes and mine craters. (Figure 3). No Man's Land was bordered by belts of barbed wire entanglements which were renewed by wiring parties working under the cover of darkness. Wire was attached to wooden or angle-iron stakes, or to the ingeniously designed screw pickets, which were less noisy to put in place at night, as they did not require hammering, but could simply be screwed into the soil. Many of these are still in use today, and are commonly encountered at field

The Great War on the Western Front

*Figure 5. Barbed wire screw pickets, still in use in France at field boundaries (left)
and in trench museums (right).*

boundaries (Figure 5).

The second line or 'support' fire trenches were at least 10 to 30 metres behind the
front line trenches, and these were in turn replaced by the final line of reserve
trenches. These were intended as second and third lines of defence, but also enabled
troops to concentrate before offensive action. The whole system could be
encapsulated within a zone of 50 to 150 metres width, but could extend to a width of
1 kilometre in some sectors, and access from the rear areas to each of the trenches in
turn was through communication trenches, which traversed the ground between the
lines of fire trenches (Figure 3). In some cases, particularly where the enemy
controlled the high ground, tunnels were constructed to allow safe passage of troops
to the front from the rear areas.

From 1915 to 1917 the Allies launched a series of offensives against the German
trench system which mostly followed the following set pattern. An artillery
bombardment marked the opening of the offensive and was intended to destroy the
defensive system of trenches, barbed wire and dug-outs. At the appointed hour,
troops would rise from the trenches ('over the top') and advance over No Man's Land
through gaps cut in their own and the German wire, which often led to dangerous
bunching. From 1916 onwards, as a protection, a 'creeping' barrage of shells
preceded the advancing troops. However, the preliminary artillery bombardment
rarely obliterated the German defensive lines, often leaving opposing artillery and

machine guns largely intact. In practice, these tactics led to little more than an initial breach of the front line before momentum was lost. More flexible trench systems and the use of small bodies of highly trained 'shock troops' (by the Germans) and massed tanks (by the Allies) led to a return to mobile warfare in 1918.

Geology and terrain in the Great War

The development of the largely static conflict on the Western Front was arguably a direct result of the increased efficiency and accuracy of artillery and machine gun fire, which reduced the effectiveness of offensive action by infantry, especially where deployed in direct frontal assault, and increased the importance of defensive positions. As a consequence, the nature of the ground fought over was extremely significant to the outcome of the war, as it was this which ultimately controlled the efficacy of defensive positions. Discriminating use of terrain has always been the hallmark of successful commanders from classical times through to the present day, but on the Western Front detailed knowledge was the key to success, and this ultimately led to the specialist surveying of topography and underlying geology by both sides.

It is generally held, echoing the views of General (later Field Marshal) Sir Douglas Haig—Commander in Chief of the British Forces on the Western Front from 1915—that the war in the west was simply a struggle for topographic position. The disposition of high ground, the relative incision of valleys, and the presence of wooded areas was of paramount importance to both attacker and defender; while the nature of the ground conditions controlled the effectiveness with which defensive trench positions could be constructed. This meant that geology, which not only ultimately controls topography but also the nature of ground conditions, was therefore one of the most important factors in the outcome of the siege warfare waged on the Western Front. The experience of warfare on the Western Front was to directly influence post-war considerations of the applications of geology in war, particularly in the fields of: (1) military resourcing (water supply and aggregates/minerals), (2) military engineering geology (construction of defences, and military mining) and, (3) strategy and tactics with respect to the ground fought over. These principles remain important on the battlefield of today, and any re-examination of past experience can only help in our level of understanding of these aspects. This field guide addresses some of the pertinent principles.

On the Western Front today, in both France and Belgium, there are several areas where aspects of the original battlefield terrain are preserved. These and other parts of the preserved battlefield have been described in many guides, such as the comprehensive *Battleground Europe* guides published by Leo Cooper, and the guides by Coombs (1990), Holt & Holt (1993, 1996, 1997) and Middlebrook

The Great War on the Western Front

& Middlebrook (1994). These guides mostly outline the nature of the preserved trenchlines, pill-boxes and the many cemeteries which are concentrated into this relatively small area of Northwestern Europe. The Holts' guides in particular are most useful, and are complemented by a pair of specially produced battlefield maps.

This fieldguide concentrates on three areas: (1) the Ypres Salient, and in particular the area from Zillebeke to Messines; (2) the Arras sector, and in particular Vimy Ridge; and (3) the Somme battlefield of 1916, and in particular the area around the Newfoundland Memorial Park at Beaumont Hamel. These are discussed below as separate itineraries, following a discussion of the general geology of the Western Front and its impact on military activities during the Great War.

Geology of the Western Front

GEOLOGY OF THE WESTERN FRONT

The geology of the British sector of the Western Front is relatively simple,
comprising as it does Upper Cretaceous chalks and Palaeogene clay and sands,
which in turn are overlain by thick sedimentary deposits of Quaternary age (Figure 6
and see Geological Time Scale p.79). The geological structure of these units is also
relatively simple with no complex folding, although some important faults are
known. This simplicity, however, belies the complexity of the underlying Palaeozoic
basement, which was extensively folded and fractured during the Hercynian
mountain building episode at the end of the Carboniferous, and which also built the
Ardennes, farther to the east. Importantly, these Palaeozoic rocks include
Westphalian Coal Measures which run in a narrow belt through the region of Lens;
the only surface expression of this are the large and imposing conical waste heaps
which surround the town. In the following section, the geology of the region is
discussed, with special reference to three areas: the Flanders Plain; the Lens
Coalfield; and Artois and Picardy—the Somme region.

The Flanders Plain

Flanders is an extensive, flat plain which has been fought over for centuries.
Geologically, the plain is mostly composed of a thick succession of Palaeogene
(largely Eocene) sediments which overlie the Chalk. These sediments are in turn
overlain by extensive sands in the coastal area, deposited during late Quaternary sea-
level rises (Figure 6).

The geological structure of the region is dominated by gentle folding, a function of
the Alpine Orogeny which affected widely the Cretaceous Chalk and overlying
Palaeogene sedimentary successions. However, overall, the structure of Flanders
and Artois is subdued, with some broad folds interrupted by faults. In Flanders an
extremely shallow asymmetric syncline extends from the Lens Coalfield in the
southeast to the coastal plain of Nieuport in the northwest (Figure 7). The axial trace
of this fold trends approximately northwest–southeast, and the largest part of the
Flanders lowland represents the flat-lying basin-centre of the syncline. Southwest of
the Douai region Mesozoic and Palaeogene sediments are folded into a smaller,
equally gently expressed syncline, the southwestern limb of which is interrupted by
the Marqueffles Fault, which throws up the underlying chalk into a northfacing fault
scarp at Vimy Ridge (Figure 7). The Marqueffles Fault is one of several in the
region which are post-Hercynian in age, and which trend broadly northwest-
southeast. Many of these faults have no surface expression, being buried by the
thick Mesozoic-Cenozoic cover, but the Marqueffles is an exception as it propagates
through the overlying cover.

The lowest exposed geological units in the Flanders region consist largely of Middle

p 78

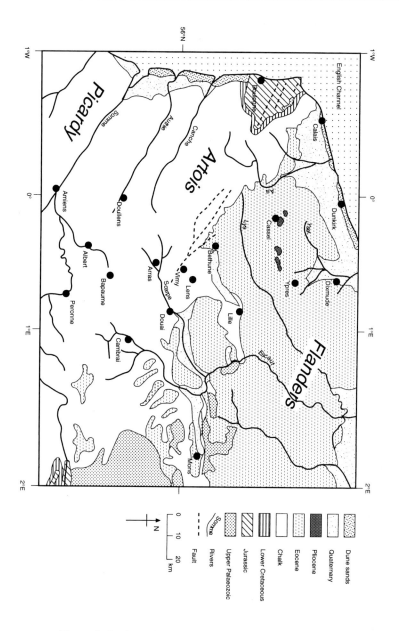

Figure 6. Geological map of Flanders, Artois and Picardy.

Geology of the Western Front

and Upper Chalk of Senonian age, and these are exposed in the region of Douai, and at Vimy Ridge which borders the Flanders Plain (Figures 6 and 7). For the most part, however, chalk is unexposed in Flanders as it lies deep beneath the covering of Palaeogene sediments. These were deposited in the large Anglo-Franco-Belgian Basin which existed from the Palaeocene to the Neogene. Much of the early work on these sediments was carried out by Dudley Stamp (later Sir Dudley Stamp), the famous geographer who, as a serving Artists Rifles and later Royal Engineer Officer, carried out some geological investigations in the region in 1918, and continued them into the early 1920's (Stamp, 1919, 1921a,b, 1922). At depth, the Middle and Upper Chalk are underlain by Chalk Marl and Palaeozoic basement. The latter in the region of Lens and La Bassée includes Upper Westphalian Coal Measures which have been worked by deep mines.

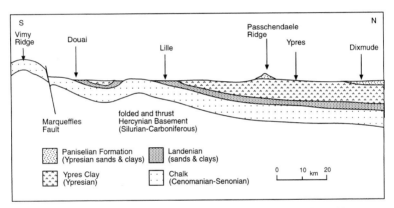

Figure 7. Sketch geological section from Dixmude (Diksmuide) to Vimy.

The Palaeogene sediments of Flanders lie on a much eroded chalk surface, produced by a widespread retreat of the sea at the end of the Cretaceous. The basal Palaeogene sediments form a complex which can only be dated approximately as Dano-Montian in age, and were deposited by a sea which reinvaded from the north. The succeeding sediments are broadly equivalent in type and age across southern England, northern France and Belgium, at least until the onset of uplift in the Artois region, which effectively separated off the Belgian and English parts of the Basin to produce the well-studied Paris Basin (e.g. Pomerol, 1982). Typically, these mostly Palaeogene sediments record successive 'pulses' of transgressive and regressive episodes; changes in relative sea - level controlled in part by the first phases of the opening of the Atlantic far to the north and in part by the developing Alpine Orogeny to the south. These transgressive-regressive cycles became famous as a consequence of the studies by Dudley Stamp, published just after his military service in Belgium (Stamp, 1921a, b).

At the base of the Palaeogene succession, overlying the poorly developed Dano-Montian sediments are Palaeocene (Landenian) glauconitic sands which are broadly equivalent in age and facies to the Thanet Sands of southeast England, and these extended further across the eroding chalk surface in France and Belgium. This transgressive episode was reversed in the later Landenian. The next major transgressive episode was sufficient to deposit marine clay from the London Basin to Flanders, north of the Artois anticline; while more lagoonal deposits were forming south of Artois in the Paris Basin. These marine clays, variously named the London Clay and the Ypres Clay—the *Argile de Flandres*—are Early Ypresian (Eocene) in age. By the later Ypresian, the Artois anticline was inundated and marine sands were deposited throughout the Anglo-Franco-Belgian Basin. Importantly, these include the clays, sands and sandy clays of the Paniselian Formation, named after Mont Panisel near Mons, and it is this collection of sediments which caps the chain of low hills which surrounds the Belgian town of Ypres. These sediments are important in allowing groundwater to propagate down to the Ypres Clay, producing spring lines which provided water for Ypres before the war (Strahan, 1917). The higher 'peaks', particularly the 'mountains of Flanders'—Mont Cassel and Mont Kemmel are examples—preserve marine and lagoonal sediments of later Eocene (Lutetian and Bartonian) and Pliocene age at their summits (Stamp, 1919).

The topography of the Flanders plain is uncomplicated, as northeast of Vimy Ridge it is broken only by a series of low hills with elevations of no greater than 50 metres. The vast majority of the Flanders Plain is floored by the Ypres Clay, and the Flanders hills form two low ridges consisting of Ypresian and Paniselian sand units representing eroded remnants of more extensive coverage of the region. In the coastal region of Flanders, these formations are overlain by Flandrian sands associated with the last major marine transgressive episode of the Quaternary, during the Holocene.

The Lens Coalfield

After 250 years of exploitation the Lens Coalfield is no longer extensively worked for coal. This is due to inherent geological difficulties presented by the nature of the reserves in the coal basin, which are buried deep under the Chalk cover, and fractured by many faults.

The Lens Coalfield trends northwest-southeast, extending from Douai to Lens and on to Bethune (Figure 8). Structurally it is complex, representing a westwards extension of the intensely folded and faulted region of the Ardennes. It was buried in the late Cretaceous by marine transgressions which deposited thick chalk units over the region. Cross-sections of the sub-Chalk basement reveal Silurian to early Carboniferous rocks affected by a stacked series of thrust slices. These faults

Geology of the Western Front

repeat the sequence of late Carboniferous rocks, superimposing several levels of productive coal-bearing sedimentary units of late Westphalian age.

The most important of these faults is the *Grande Faille du Midi,* which is usually buried and effectively delimits the southern margin of the Westphalian coalfield (Figure 8). The thrust slices are in turn cut through by many normal faults, many of which are buried but some of which have a surface expression, propagated as they are through the Mesozoic cover (Figure 8).

The late Westphalian sandstones, silts and shales, and interbedded coal seams up to 1.6 metres thick, were mostly deposited in coastal lagoons, which were occasionally susceptible to marine flooding. Both during coal deposition and after, these basins were affected by the great mountain building episode of the Hercynian Orogeny which helped construct the Ardennes, as well as the related London-Brabant Massif, which itself is now buried deep under the Mesozoic cover in south-central England. Erosion and weathering of these land masses during the Mesozoic, accompanied by subsequent sea-level rises, led to their eventual flooding in the Cretaceous, when a

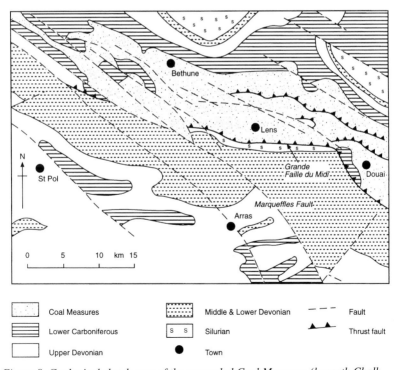

Figure 8. Geological sketch map of the concealed Coal Measures (beneath Chalk cover) of the Lens Coalfield.

thick succession of chalk was deposited.

Topographically, the Lens Coalfield is indistinguishable from the Flanders lowland. Its location is, however, easy to discern due to the presence of the almost volcanic-looking peaks of coal waste which sit on the otherwise flat landscape. These 'peaks' were extensively used in the war for battlefield observation. Today, some are used for recreational purposes—particularly dry ski runs—while many others are in the process of being reclaimed, and it is likely that over the course of the years only the small clusters of mining cottages will give testimony to the former presence of a mining industry in the region.

Artois and Picardy—The Somme Region

The Artois region exposes the Chalk in a broad anticlinal structure which is effectively an extension of the Weald anticline in southern England. Today Artois forms a dissected chalk plain with some preserved remnants of Palaeogene sediments, and is covered by a thick blanket of Quaternary sediments (Figure 6). In reality, chalk is only to be seen exposed currently in quarries, road cuts and river valleys, although chalky soil is a common feature of the region. However, during the war, chalk was exposed where trenches intercepted it, and the resulting white snaking lines and chalky spoil parapets were obvious sights for aerial observers.

The Artois 'anticline' is in effect an uplifted block which has a relatively simple geological structure. It comprises a series of open northwest-southeast trending folds, although for much of the region the beds are almost flat-lying. Although subdued, these shallow flexures have a dramatic effect on the drainage pattern, with parallel rivers flowing along the axial areas of the synclines. The chalks of the Somme are broadly equivalent in lithology to those of southern England, comprising three broad divisions: an upper, flintless, unit; a middle, flint-bearing unit, and a clay-rich lower unit. The oldest Artois chalks are Cenomanian in age and are developed as conglomeratic layers overlying the Palaeozoic rocks beneath. They record the marine inundation of the Hercynian basement. These layers are rarely exposed. More important, particularly with regard to water supply, is the presence of the overlying impermeable marly unit, formed by chalks of early to middle Turonian age. These marly chalks are most commonly exposed in valley bottoms and their clay component tends to give them a blueish hue when freshly cut. This useful lithological clue aided wartime geologists in identifying them in boreholes during water supply investigations (King, 1921a, b).

Later Turonian chalks are less clay-rich and are characterised by an abundance of large flints in distinct lines. Chalks of Senonian (Coniacian-Santonian) age are purer in composition, more porous and whiter in colour, with little in the way of a clay component. They have disseminated flints only in their basal part, the upper part

Geology of the Western Front

Figure 9. Senonian Chalk on the Somme. Top, quarry near Beaucourt showing flint lines. Bottom, solution hollows and overlying limon complex near Mametz.

Geology of the Western Front

comprising chalk alone (Figure 9). The boundary between the clay-rich Turonian chalks and the flint-bearing Turonian-Senonian chalks is of great hydrogeological significance, and determining the nature of the boundary was a task for military geologists of the day (King, 1921a, b). According to their contemporary accounts, where the boundary was brought close to the surface by folding, water extraction was of the order of 1000 gallons hourly, while where the water table was mostly developed in thick Senonian chalks, extraction reached a maximum of around 12,000 gallons hourly.

Influences of the Quaternary, especially its older Pleistocene part, are felt in this region in the fact that the surface of the Artois chalk is mostly frost shattered and it is typically overlain by at least four geological deposits of Quaternary age: Pleistocene clay-with-flints, loess and loam, and Holocene alluvium—although not all will be present at any given location (Figure 9). In some cases, residual Palaeogene Landenian deposits are also recorded beneath the Quaternary deposits, particularly the glauconitic Louvil Sands which are broadly equivalent in age and facies to the Thanet Sands of southern England. Another characteristic of the Chalk region is the widespread occurrence of sarsens; silica-cemented sand units representing the erosional remnants of formerly more extensive Palaeogene deposits. The sarsens are extremely durable and were widely used in road construction, as they are still to this day throughout Artois.

The clay-with-flints is developed over parts of the Somme area and is a result of weathering of the chalk, which leaves a clay residue studded with durable flints. The thickness of this deposit is variable, from less than a metre to up to 10 metres, with the thickest deposits capping the upland areas. Loess caps the clay-with-flints and is in turn covered by a clay-rich sand or loam. The origin of the loess is as a fine, wind-blown sediment derived from vegetation-free periglacial areas which developed in front of the extensive glaciers of the last ice age. The loess is often reworked by water to produce a valuable brick earth, widely used in brick making. However, the loess and loam are often classified together on French maps as *limons des plateaux,* which comprises several layers of sand and gravels. The *limon* constitutes a fine covering on the upland areas, but sometimes reaches a thickness of 10 metres, thinning out at the margins. It is commonly reworked by hill wash processes to form much of the alluvium present in most of the valley bottoms. The loess is a fine-grained sand unit and is porous, while the loam contains a higher percentage of clay. As reported by Aubrey Strahan in 1917, then Director of the Geological Survey, it was with this deposit that the men were mostly in contact in the trenches and dug-outs, and tellingly, 'which is in evidence on the clothes of those returning from the Front', the mud of the Somme clinging to the uniforms of the troops.

The Somme region is typical of a dissected chalk upland which is effectively

Geology of the Western Front

starved of surface water and a consequence of this is the large number of hamlets clustered around wells and other water supplies; this contrasts with the more scattered and isolated farms in Flanders, where surface water is more plentiful. Several rivers dissect the upland and show a strong parallel alignment, controlled by the underlying structure of the Chalk. Many dry valleys, some of them deeply incised, are also found within the region. The Chalk is deeply fissured, but there are no natural cave systems developed within the area, although there are several underground systems which have been created since prehistory by human activities. Where clay-with-flints cap the Chalk, water is retained leaving a heavy soil which is often uncultivated, except for forestry. Many of the wooded areas of the Somme battlefield lie in soils developed in clay-with-flints, and these woods were to be important focal points for battles on the Somme in 1916. The loess and loam (*limon*) units are more often cultivated, and the loam helps define the character of the region, with the Chalk forming most of the valleys in the region, whereas the loess and loam caps the hills and extends down the intermediate slopes.

GEOLOGY AND WARFARE ON THE WESTERN FRONT

Geologists with the British Army

The need for the establishment of a geological staff in the British armies was
recognised in April 1915 and by May 1916 the British had two geologists who were
attached to the Royal Engineers: Lieutenant (later Captain) W.B.R. King (Royal
Welch Fusiliers, attached Royal Engineers) working to the Chief Engineer, and
Major (later Lieutenant Colonel) T.W. Edgeworth David (Australian Mining Corps),
working under the Inspector of Mines. The responsibilities of this small
establishment lay predominantly in the areas of water supply (King), and military
mining and dug-out construction (David). In late 1916 and in 1918, three more
geologists, seconded from the tunnelling companies, were attached to this staff. By
contrast, the Germans in this sector are known to have had a large geological
establishment which, for example, had the benefit of the local geological information
available within the occupied city of Lille (see also Rose & Rosenbaum, 1993, 1998
and Macleod, 1995).

Military resources: water supply

Sufficient potable water for troops, horses and pack animals was of great importance
to the armies engaged in all theatres of the war, and providing an adequate supply
was a significant problem on the Western Front. In the majority of cases it was hard
to maintain water supply to the front line troops, most of which had to be brought
forward from rear areas in containers. Such transport of water supplies from rear
areas was costly in time and effort and therefore a major task for the Royal
Engineers was an investigation of local water supplies through boreholes.
Lieutenant King was largely responsible for water supply investigations in the
British sector of the Western Front, the results of which were published after the war,
both anonymously by the Royal Engineers (Institution of Royal Engineers, 1921)
and by King himself (King, 1919, 1921a, b).

In the Ypres area, peace-time water supply was largely derived from surface water in
lakes, fed in part from springs emanating from the base of the Paniselian sediments,
together with shallow wells tapping water perched on the Ypres Clay and other clays
in the sands, surface loams and alluvium. Water supply for the troops was similarly
obtained through purification of surface water supplies and through borings. Other
supplementary supplies were obtained from Landenian sands, often referred to as
'Thanet Sands' in contemporary accounts, which lie on more clay-rich Landenian
deposits mantling the Chalk, and which are up to 35 metres from the surface beneath
the thick Ypres Clay. Multiple boreholes were made allowing accurate estimates of
the depth to the aquifer (King, 1921a, b).

Geology and Warfare on the Western Front

In the Somme region, where surface water is relatively rare in the chalk uplands, maintenance of a sufficient water supply was dependent on boring to the saturated chalk below the water table and on pipe lines. However, the position and shape of this water table was known to be variable, rising under the hills and sinking towards the main river valleys and constrained by the underlying marly chalks. The height of the water table was found to be in direct relationship with the amount of rainfall and evaporation, particularly in the winter when rainfall was at its maximum and evaporation at its minimum. In the main river valleys the flowing water is mostly fed by springs, while in most of the upland areas the valleys are dry. In order to have a good water yield it was necessary for boreholes to penetrate into a thickness of *c.* 20 metres of permeable, water-bearing (i.e. beneath the water table) chalk.

Military resources: aggregates

The survey and exploitation of locally-derived aggregates was of great importance on the Western Front, as the static condition of the lines meant that enough resources had to be available for the construction of new roads and for concrete emplacements.

Aggregates for road construction were mostly obtained from northern France and Brittany, outside the immediate area of operations on the Western Front. Quaternary river gravels in the valleys of the Authie and Grouches rivers near Doullens were examined for road stone extraction and it was estimated that they had a yield of approximately 500,000 tons. Another potential source of road stone were the 'sarsens' (sand concretions) scattered over the surface of the Chalk, remnants from the now denuded Palaeogene sands of the Somme region. These had been widely used in pre-war pavé road construction and estimates suggested that the Somme region could supply a potential yield of 50 million tons of sarsen stone.

Aggregates for concrete emplacements for both opposing forces in the British sector of the Western Front were also mostly derived from outside the immediate area of operations, quite simply because there were few suitable materials. The Germans made extensive use of 'pill boxes' and other concrete emplacements in the Ypres region and aggregate resourcing for this was a considerable problem. For example, the British geological establishment, and particularly the Geological Survey, were involved in forensic investigations of the provenance of aggregates in captured German positions (Institution of Royal Engineers, 1922a; Sabine, 1991; Oldham, 1995). Typically, aggregates used by the Germans in concrete emplacements on the Passchendaele Ridge contained Rhine basalt pebbles and other distinctive rock types, that had clearly been transported considerable distances through Holland from the Rhine. This was an infringement of Dutch neutrality, a matter which caused some debate in Parliament and a flurry of diplomatic communications.

Geology and Warfare on the Western Front

Military engineering geology: defensive works

Given the nature of the largely static warfare waged on the Western Front, the construction of habitable trenches and dug-outs was of great importance. On the British front, the Royal Engineers were responsible for site investigations of ground suitable for dug-out construction and concrete emplacements. Little detailed site investigation of British trench positions was carried out, most often because in most cases there was a need for rapid deployment and protection of troops, especially after offensive actions. However, site investigations for dug-outs were more extensive, particularly in reserve areas, where they contained headquarters and medical staffs. The results of these site investigations, mostly carried out by Major Edgworth David in conjunction with Lieutenant King and a small additional staff, were published in a series of specially annotated geological maps for the whole of the battlefront. These surveys plotted standard 'solid' and 'drift' geology at a scale of 1:10,000, but were primarily summaries of suitability of ground for the construction of defensive positions, particularly dug-outs. Formations were mapped in the usual manner, but were denoted on the map in shades of blue or red, depending on whether they were suitable or unsuitable (i.e. water-bearing or permeable) for dug-out construction (Institution of Royal Engineers, 1922a).

Trenches. Trench construction was usually carried out by labour battalions and fatigue parties of 'resting' front line troops. These parties had mostly to dig their trenches rapidly under the cover of darkness, generally with men spaced between two to three paces apart. Speed of digging was directly influenced by ground conditions, prevailing weather, and the condition of the troops. Little reference to the local geological conditions was made, but it is clear that the success and ease of trench construction was directly influenced by three factors: (1) the position relative to slope; (2) the nature of the underlying geological material, and; (3) the relative position of the water table (e.g. Brooks, 1920).

Position relative to slope was important in the construction of trenches. Basic principles for entrenchment were laid down in the British Field Service Regulations, which emphasised theoretical aspects of position in relation to forward and reverse slopes, valleys and spurs, and topographical height. These aspects were considered important in order to allow effective observation of opposing trench positions, to prevent enemy observation of forward and reserve trenches, and to provide necessary supportive arcs of fire for small arms. Ideally, the trench lines were to be designed to contour hills and valleys, particularly significant in providing 'mutual enfilade' fire in valleys, the assaulting troops being attacked by the defenders from both sides of the valley, and on the slopes of spurs (Figure 10). The ideal situation was to place artillery observation and machine gun posts at the highest points. For example, on a ridge the observation points should ideally have been at the crest of the slope, the firing lines being forward of them, down the 'forward' slope. Where

Geology and Warfare on the Western Front

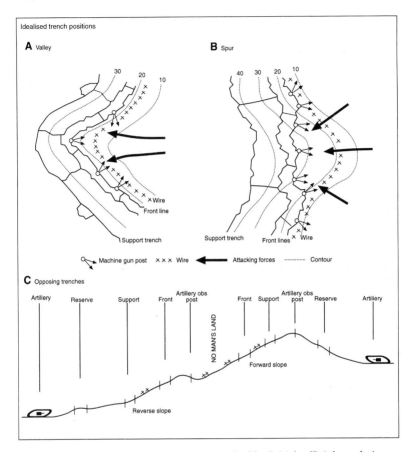

Figure 10. Idealised trench positions, as prescribed by British official regulations.

only the reverse slope of a ridge was held, the observation line was to be positioned to the front of the fire trenches, just cresting the ridge. In all cases, the positioning relative to slope was to maximise observation of the enemy so as to direct artillery and machine gun fire accurately. In the Ypres area, in most cases, the British trench lines were positioned either at the foot of or on the reverse slopes of ridges formed by the Paniselian Formation overlying the Ypres Clay. This made artillery observation difficult and provided ample opportunity for accurate offensive fire from the German artillery. This was also the case at Vimy Ridge, a chalk fault scarp which provided cover for assault troops, and which was only taken with the assistance of offensive mining in 1917. In the rolling chalk upland of the Somme,

Geology and Warfare on the Western Front

British positions were more variably positioned and more able to follow the guidelines laid down by the official regulations.

The nature of the underlying material and the position of the water table controlled both the ease of digging and the capability of the trench sides to retain intact without slumping. In the Ypres area, trenches were cut in clays or poorly consolidated Palaeogene sands (Figures 4 and 11) and were therefore likely to slump or flow, and considerable revetment with wattle, sandbags or corrugated sheet iron was necessary. Trench drainage was difficult, especially where cut into the impermeable Ypres Clay (Figure 11). Pumping was usually necessary and was a demanding and difficult task. Where trenches did not penetrate either the Ypres Clay or the clay units of the Paniselian Formation some drainage was possible, but trenches cut through water-saturated sands, such as the Kemmel Sands of the Paniselian, usually led to trench failure and slumping. On the Somme, trenches usually penetrated either the thick loess, loam and clay-with-flints or were cut into the frost-shattered surface units of the chalk. As with the trenches dug in the Ypres area these were largely incapable of retaining trench side definition and needed revetment, except in those rare cases where trench sides penetrated sound chalk. Drainage was problematic only where trenches were floored by impermeable clay-with-flints or where trenches were deep enough to penetrate the zone of water saturated chalk.

Dug-outs. Dug-outs are underground shelters intended for a variety of uses, and their usefulness was largely controlled by local geology (Figure 12). They may also be classified according to the depth to which they penetrate. Three basic types used by the British can be recognised: (1) shallow recesses ('funk holes') cut into the walls of the trench, giving limited protection; (2) cut and cover shelters, roofed with strong corrugated iron sheeting ('elephant iron') and sand bags, giving some protection from indirect artillery fire, and; (3) deep shelters with overhead cover provided by the natural geology. Shallow recesses were mostly cut into trench sides, and were constrained by the same factors as influenced trench construction. Those cut into sand units commonly gave limited protection, needing considerable revetment to stop movement. Flooding was a problem where such dug-outs were at trench floor level (Figure 11). Cut and cover dug-outs were essentially covered over trenches, with the same attendant problems. Deep shelters, the most desirable type, were intended to withstand direct shellfire and therefore needed an adequate cover of undisturbed rock as a roof, usually between a minimum of two metres for light artillery fire and 16 metres to withstand heavy fire. Concrete shelters constructed at surface level were an alternative to the construction of deep dug-outs.

In the Ypres area, satisfactory deep shelters could be constructed at depth in the impermeable Ypres Clay or within the basal clay units of the Paniselian Formation (Figure 11). On the slopes of the Passchendaele and Messines ridges the water-bearing Kemmel Sands of the Paniselian Formation were apt to flow and were

Geology and Warfare on the Western Front

Figure 11. Trenches and dug-outs exposed in foundation works near Ypres. The trenches (right) were cut in Paniselian sands overlying Ypres Clay; the dug-out (left) is 10 metres deep in Ypres Clay and is flooded, a function of the junction between the permeable sands and impermeable clay.

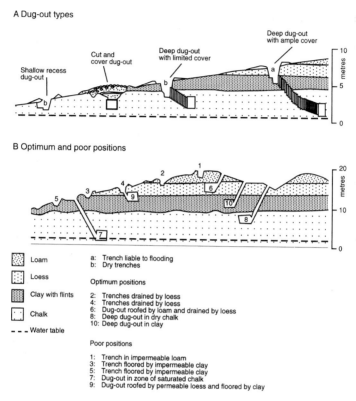

A Dug-out types

B Optimum and poor positions

	Loam
	Loess
	Clay with flints
	Chalk
– – –	Water table

a: Trench liable to flooding
b: Dry trenches

Optimum positions

2: Trenches drained by loess
4: Trenches drained by loess
6: Dug-out roofed by loam and drained by loess
8: Deep dug-out in dry chalk
10: Deep dug-out in clay

Poor positions

1: Trench in impermeable loam
3: Trench floored by impermeable clay
5: Trench floored by impermeable clay
7: Dug-out in zone of saturated chalk
9: Dug-out roofed by permeable loess and floored by clay

Figure 12. Dug-out type and positions relative to geology.

incapable of retaining the integrity of the dug-out walls, although the overlying sandy clay units were more suitable. On the Somme, deep dug-out construction was limited by the depth to water table, which varied according to season and maximum rainfall. The depth to saturated chalk was estimated through a programme of borings intended for the task. Shallow dug-outs could be constructed in the overlying Quaternary deposits, as long as they did not cross boundaries between water bearing and impermeable units, leading to springs.

Military engineering geology: offensive mining

Geological advice to the British army on military mining was the responsibility of Major Edgworth David. A considerable literature has grown about the activities of miners during the war, and some of this is listed in the suggested reading section. In essence, military mines may be defined as any underground system intended for offensive action through explosion or defensive action to counter enemy mining.

Geology and Warfare on the Western Front

Tunnels are intended for shelter and for troop movements underground. Mining and tunnelling were carried out by the mining companies which consisted of men mostly recruited directly from sewer workers and from the collieries and mineral mines of Britain and the Empire. Five companies were originally raised for the Royal Engineers in 1915, growing to thirty by the end of the war. Mining was also extensively exercised by the Germans and, although debatable, it has been reported that this may have been without recourse to sound geological advice. In any case, by 1916, mine galleries were constructed in over 30 miles (48km) of the British front and in that year approximately 1500 mines were fired.

In Flanders mining was inhibited by the nature of the subcrop of clays and sands. Surrounding Ypres successful mining was mostly restricted to the Ypres Clay or to the overlying clays of the Paniselian Formation. The clay was worked by hand by miners using the 'clay kicking' method (see page 33) to avoid noise and subsequent countermining by the Germans. Mechanical extraction was attempted, but was abandoned, and at least one boring machine remains underground today. Above these clay units the sands and sandy clays of the Paniselian Formation and the Quaternary were mostly found to be too water saturated to work, the water perched on the clay below. The Kemmel Sands of the Paniselian Formation, for example, are subject to high pore water pressure leading to significant fluidity, and this prevented successful shallow mining operations in this sector, typical mine depths being between 20-30 metres. On the Somme, successful mining operations were largely restricted by the height of the water table within the Chalk. As discussed above, this varied according to topography and according to season, but was predictable with reference to maximum rainfall and run off/evaporation rates.

Tactical considerations of topography

A classic concept of the war on the Western Front is that of a succession of attritional battles for high ground, such as the Passchendaele Offensive of July 1917, which sought to drive the Germans from their commanding position on the Passchendaele Ridge, east of Ypres. Clearly, topography and the nature of ground conditions were major considerations in the planning of any offensive action. However, it is important to understand that the situation of Allied trench systems was often greatly influenced by the General Staff's offensive policy and unwillingness to yield ground. The Allies (France, Britain and its Empire, Belgium, and later, Portugal and the USA) were fighting on French and Belgian soil and were on the tactical defensive, a situation which could only be reversed by a sustained tactical offensive. The Germans, on the other hand, had gained ground early in the war and were able to retain their position through maintenance of an overall defensive attitude, notable exceptions being the early battles for Ypres in 1914-1915, the Battle for Verdun in 1916 and the Spring offensives in 1918. In practical terms this equated with an unwillingness, in the early parts of the war at least, of the Allies to construct

Geology and Warfare on the Western Front

permanent and sophisticated positions providing safe accommodation for the troops, and of an inability to actively select in advance the best tactical position for the trench lines. Therefore, deep shelters designed to protect troops from direct shellfire were mostly a feature of German defensive positions, while Allied positions had mostly small excavations in trench walls, or later, cut and cover shelters using corrugated iron and sandbags. This meant in many cases that Allied lines were poorly situated with respect to topography and ground conditions, while German policy allowed for strategic withdrawal to carefully prepared and suitably located positions, as demonstrated by their retreat to the Hindenberg Line in 1917.

Three important terrain factors may be identified: (1) the location of trench systems with respect to the topographic relief, which directly influenced their safety through exposure of troops to direct observation and enemy artillery or small arms fire; (2) the location of defensive positions with respect to the solid and drift geology, and the maintenance of the health, safety and well-being of the troops contained within them and; (3) the nature of ground conditions in influencing the movement of troops, equipment, and later, tanks. With all three factors, accurate knowledge of topography and ground conditions was essential. This led to a series of detailed suitability surveys in the British area of operations and to the production a large body of trench, geological, hydrological and ground suitability maps which were produced during the war, and which are now avidly collected.

ITINERARY I: THE YPRES SALIENT 1914-1918

The British battles in Flanders were concentrated from late 1914 to 1918 in an arc (salient) defending the Belgian town of Ypres. The **First and Second Battles of Ypres** (October-November 1914 and April-May 1915) were German offensives which established them on the high ground (*c.* 50 metres above sea-level) which surrounds Ypres in an arc to the east of the town. The Second Battle of Ypres is most notably associated with the first large-scale use of poison gas in the war. The **Third Battle of Ypres** (July-November 1917) was a largely British offensive intended to drive the Germans from their commanding positions and push on to take the Channel Ports of Ostend, Zeebruge and ultimately Antwerp. A prelude to this was the capture of the Messines-Wytschaete Ridge to the southeast of the town during the **Battle of Messines** in June 1917, largely through the success of military mining operations. The itinerary examines the Ypres Salient and concentrates largely upon the offensives of 1917, conflicts which forever will be associated in the British consciousness as a battle through mud, although some of the aspects of the 1915 battles will also be examined (Figure 13). The following itinerary can be achieved in a single day, although the amount of time spent at a given locality is a subject of personal preference. Ypres is a good starting point and an excellent location for a break.

Ypres (Ieper)

Ypres (Ieper) was one of the most important centres of British activity during the Great War and it is estimated that during the period of 1914-1917 there were at least 420,000 British casualties, and a similar number of German ones, in the Ypres Salient. Before the war Ypres had been a prosperous and bustling town; the war raised it to the ground, and although Ypres was never lost to the Germans, it was destroyed through artillery bombardment, a direct consequence of the German domination of the surrounding heights. The town was rebuilt after the war, much in the style of the original, with the Mediaeval Cloth Hall rising from its original foundations, and once again it is pleasant and thriving, and a focal point for visitors to the Western Front (Figure 14).

Important for most visitors to the Salient is the **Menin Gate,** which marks the start of the **Menin Road** (now the N8; Figure 13). Throughout the British occupation of the Ypres Salient the Menin Road was a strategically important route, the possession of which was contested in all of the major battles. This was a consequence of its position on the main axis of the arcuate Ypres Salient, crossing the Flanders plain and rising over the Passchendaele Ridge (Figure 13). Ypres itself lies on a flat plain formed almost exclusively of Ypres Clay, a material which is, for all intents and purposes, the equivalent of the London Clay. As in some London and east Essex gardens, this material produces a heavy clay soil, a soil which has the potential to

Itinerary I: The Ypres Salient 1914-1918

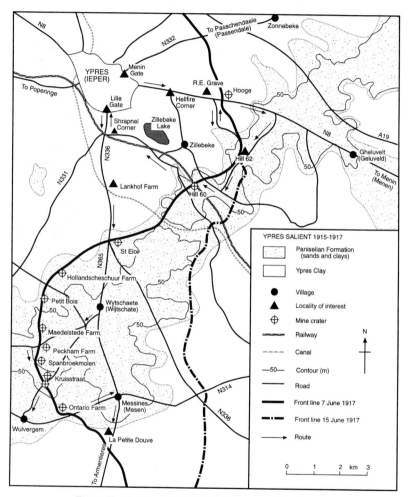

Figure 13. The Ypres Salient, 1915-17; route and locality map.

Itinerary I: The Ypres Salient 1914-1918

produce a thick glutinous mud if sufficiently water saturated and disturbed; clearly the scene was set, given the bombardments that were to follow in 1917, for the production of the nightmarish landscape which was to haunt many of the old soldiers who served in the Salient.

Figure 14. Reconstructed landmarks of the Western Front. The Cloth Hall, Ypres (left) and the Basilica of the Golden Virgin, Albert (right).

The Menin Gate commemorates the battles for Ypres and, importantly, those soldiers of Britain and the Empire who died in the Salient and have no known grave. The Gate is in the form of an arch, and was designed by Sir Reginald Blomfeld with sculpture by Sir William Reid Dick. The arch itself required extensive foundation works because of the presence of Quaternary sands overlying the Ypres Clay. It is constructed from French limestones, with panels of Portland Stone inscribed with the names of 54,900 missing from the battles of 1914-1917. The missing of later battles in the Salient, some 34,888 names, are inscribed on a separate memorial designed by Sir Herbert Baker which is to the rear of the largest CWGC cemetery in the world— **Tyne Cot Cemetery,** to the northwest of Ypres, near the village of Passchendaele (Passendale). Every evening at the Menin Gate, at 8.00 pm sharp, the traffic is stopped and the Last Post is sounded in memory of the dead, as it has done, more or less continuously (with the exception of the German occupation in 1940-45), since the memorial was unveiled in 1927.

Ypres is a good starting point for tours of the Salient. Pay-and-display parking is available in the Grote Markt, as well as in the vicinity of the Cloth Hall. There are many bars and cafes in the square and public toilets are to be found at the rear of the Cloth Hall, close to the entrance to the high-concept *'In Flanders Fields'* Museum which tells the story of the Salient. A little costly to enter, this museum nevertheless uses a wide range of current museum technologies to present the sights and sounds of the Salient. Ypres has a one way traffic system which is a little confusing, partially a function of the attractive repaving of the Grote Markt with a wide range of cobbles. Access to the east of Ypres and the **Passchendaele Ridge** which bounds it is by the Menin Road, but the Menin Gate admits only incoming traffic, so it is essential to follow signs to Menin (Menen) in order to get on the right track (Figure 13).

Hill 62 and Hooge

In travelling east from Ypres along the Menin Road, two important sites are reached: **Hill 62,** on the crest of the Passchendaele Ridge, and **Hooge**, a battlefield site now mostly overshadowed by the events of 1916 and 1917, but the site of fierce fighting in 1915 (Figure 13).

The Passchendaele Ridge effectively bounds Ypres to the east and is actually composed of a chain of low lying hills which barely reach an altitude of 50-60 metres above sea-level, the exception being **Mont Kemmel** to the southwest of Ypres, which attains a height of 150 metres. The geology of the Passchendaele Ridge is simple, consisting primarily of horizontally bedded clays and sands of the **Paniselian Formation,** which comformably overlie the clay of the Flanders Plain. The Paniselian Formation is named after its typical development at Mont Panisel, near Mons, and comprises several units of sandy clay alternating with sands. Of these units perhaps the most significant are the **Kemmel Sands** which overlie the basal clay layers of the Paniselian Formation and have a high pore pressure with percolating water perched on the impermeable clays beneath. The Kemmel Sands are capped by sandy clays, followed by the well-drained **Wytschaete Sands,** which form the upper parts of the ridge. Other 'peaks' in this chain of Paniselian hills are actually capped by Lutetian and even Pliocene sediments (Stamp, 1919). Finally, the Passchendaele Ridge has a covering of Quaternary sands, which reach a considerable thickness to the south of the ridge in the valley of the Steenbeek, south of Kruistraat. The main ridge actually acts as a watershed, with a number of small rivers converging to the northwest, near Ypres, and southeast of the ridge, towards Warneton. The Passchendaele Ridge and its spur the Messines-Wytschaete Ridge is extensively wooded, while the flat-lying Flanders Plain is mostly agricultural.

Hooge (t'Hoge on some maps) is situated about 4 km east of Ypres centre on the main Menin Road (the N8) and to approach it **Hellfire Corner** is passed, a once shell-blasted road junction, now a roundabout (Figure 13). Hellfire Corner was a significant junction during the war and is now marked by a red granite 'Demarcation

Itinerary I: The Ypres Salient 1914-1918

Stone' erected in the 1920s to mark the maximum German advance in 1918. It is one of twelve such stones in the Salient and it is notable for its sculptural detail, displaying items of military equipment and surmounted by a British 'Tommy's' helmet (Figure 15).

Figure 15. Red granite Demarcation Stone at Hellfire Corner, near Ypres.

Hooge itself lies close to the junction of the Ypres Clay and the overlying Paniselian Formation and was the scene of a hotly contested mine crater blown by the British in 1915 (Figure 13). This mine, cut by the 175th Tunnelling Company R.E., was dug through the relatively sound Ypres Clay by 'clay-kickers' and was blown using 3500 lbs of ammonal explosive on 19th July 1915, the resulting crater forming part of the front line from this point onwards (Figure 16). 'Clay kicking' was the most often used method of digging tunnels and mines in the Ypres Salient and involved the use of a cross-shaped board which enabled the miner to lie on his back and using a specially adapted spade, kick upwards at the face to remove the clay. The mine crater at Hooge exists as an ornamental pond in the grounds of the Hotel Kasteel (adjacent to the Bellewaarde Theme Park) nearby (Figure 16). South of the Menin Road is the **Hooge Crater CWGC Cemetery**, featuring a symbolic crater in its design. Other mine craters are much in evidence in the region and, just before

Itinerary I: The Ypres Salient 1914-1918

reaching Hooge, a road to the right marked with a green CWGC sign to **Railway Wood R.E. Grave** is a worthy detour to see one of several small water-filled mine craters dug in the Ypres Clay and blown in Paniselian Sands (Figure 13 and 16). This location is marked by a simple memorial to members of the 177th Tunnelling Company R.E. who lost their lives underground here and whose remains lie beneath the simple monument (Figure 16). At Hooge itself there is a good, well-signposted museum (housed in a former chapel; an entrance fee is payable) which is well worth a visit, and which has an attached bar and toilets.

Figure 16. Mine craters in the Ypres Salient. Left, crater at Railway Wood, R.E. Grave; right, Hooge Crater in the grounds of Hotel Kasteel.

Hill 62 ('Mount Sorrel') and its trench museum is reached by a small road (Canadalaan—Maple Avenue) leading up the Passchendaele Ridge, south from the main Ypres-Menin road (the N8; Figure 13). The turn off is close to the Hooge Museum, just before the Canada Cafe, and is signposted with a distinctive Canadian Battlefield Memorial sign. The turn is rather sharp and can be easily missed. Hill 62 is one of several high points on the Passchendaele Ridge which enabled the Germans, who had captured it in 1915, to overlook the British. Throughout the war the British stubbornly held on to the town of Ypres and its Salient, despite the more realistic suggestion in 1915 of a strategic withdrawal to the west of the town by General Sir Herbert Plumer. This would have shortened the line and reduced German observation of activities, but would have been a political disaster, relinquishing as it would have one of the last Belgian towns in allied hands.

Several names have been applied to the high point at Hill 62 and, unfortunately, many are incorrect and misleading; Hill 62 (62 metres above sea-level) is the most accurate. The hill itself is developed in Paniselian sands and clays, which vary from being relatively dry to relatively wet (Figure 17). The British line rose up the hill

Itinerary I: The Ypres Salient 1914-1918

through the wooded area (**Sanctuary Wood,** so called because it was served as gathering place for stragglers in the early battles of 1914), with the German line inhabiting the ridge top. The memorial marks the defence of Sanctuary Wood by the Canadians, who held the line from Hill 60 to Hooge in the face of a fierce offensive by the Germans in June 1916—referred to by the Canadians as the Battle of Sanctuary Wood. The viewpoint at the top of the hill, presently called **Mount Sorrel** (named after Montsorrel in Leicestershire) despite the fact that this prominence lay farther to the southwest, provides an indication of why the 'heights' of the Passchendaele Ridge were so fiercely contested for. A monument with orientation signs provides a good opportunity to observe the salient from its most westerly extension. The monument is itself is carved from granite, with paving slabs of Carboniferous limestone—the Black Marble of Dinant, and a range of other Belgian stones.

Figure 17. Sanctuary Wood with Hill 62 (Mount Sorrel) in the distance, October 1917. Reproduced with permission of the Trustees of the Imperial War Museum, negative no. E(AUS) 1234.

On the lower slopes of the hill are the best-preserved trenches with public access in Belgium, and arguably the whole of the Western Front (see front cover). This trench museum, which is open all year and is entered through the bar (requiring the payment of a small entry fee), preserves a section of the British and Canadian front line from 1916-17. In this open air museum the nature of the trenches, divided into fire bays to prevent enfilading fire, can really be appreciated (Figure 4). Shell holes and a few supported tree trunks from the original Sanctuary Wood make up the remainder of the open air part of the museum. The sandy nature of the soil developed on the Paniselian Formation can be examined, as can the fact there is often standing water in the trenches and shell holes, inhibited by clay levels; and it is not hard to imagine the discomfort of living in these 'muddy ditches'. The indoor part of the museum contains some interesting artefacts, including stereoviewers of contemporary photographs showing life on the Western Front, including some fairly gruesome scenes.

Farther down the road back towards Ypres and Hooge is the **Sanctuary Wood CWGC Cemetery**, with many men killed in the battles on and around Hill 62. Notable is the private memorial to Lieutenant Keith Rae, killed in a flame-thrower attack at Hooge in 1915; the grave of Lieutenant Gilbert Talbot, son of the Bishop of London, after whom Talbot House in Poperinge was named; and the grave of Hauptman Hans Roser, a German aviator shot down by Captain Lanoe George Hawker, in the action that led to the award of a V.C. to Hawker. Hawker himself was later to fall victim to Baron von Richthofen, and has no known grave.

Figure 18. Mine craters on the north side of Hill 60 in August 1917. Reproduced with permission of the Trustees of the Imperial War Museum, negative no. E(AUS) 581.

Itinerary I: The Ypres Salient 1914-1918

Hill 60

Rejoining the N8 and travelling west, the Hooge crater is passed by on the left and Hooge Crater CWGC Cemetery on the right to cross the front line of early 1917. Turning right at a junction (referred to as **Clapham Junction** during the war) which is denoted by two divisional memorials, the north of Sanctuary Wood and Hill 62 is traversed passing along Pappotstraat, which more or less follows the ridge top, to Zillebeke, and turning left at the T-junction until the well-signposted Hill 60 is reached (Figure 13). **Hill 60** is arguably one of the most bitterly fought over pimples on the surface of the Ypres Salient and is effectively preserved as a war grave by the Commonwealth War Graves Commission.

Hill 60, like Hill 62, was so named because it was 60 metres above sea - level. In fact, Hill 60 is partially an artificial mound of spoil dug when the adjacent railway cutting was constructed. South of the Hill is another, more linear, feature constructed of spoil, known as the **Caterpillar**, and this was also intensely fought over. The spoil tip which forms the body of Hill 60 rests upon the Paniselian clays and sandy clays and was the scene of intense mining activity by both sides from 1915 through to 1917 (Ball, 1919). The site itself comprises heavily broken ground and many craters can be mapped, a testimony to the intensity of the mining activities (Figure 18). According to the Holts (Holt & Holt, 1997), Hill 60 was probably the site of the first British mine of the war, blown in February 1915; and this was to be followed by several other mines in later months. The 1915 craters are observable in the main site and built into these are a number of pill-boxes, most of which were destroyed during the later mining activities of 1917 (Figure 19). These German pillboxes or concrete shelters had their entrances pointing east to protect against British shellfire. Examination of the aggregate mix of these concrete structures demonstrates a variety of lithic clasts, particularly basalt pebbles, and some of these were examined by geologists at the Geological Survey in 1917 demonstrating that Rhine gravels had been imported by barge via Holland—a clear breach of neutrality (Sabine, 1991; Oldham, 1995). The most prominent concrete structure is a British observation post—the observation slit facing east—which was built by the 4th Australian Engineers in early 1918 on top of an existing German pill box (Figures 19, 20). The aggregate mix in this later structure contrasts very strongly, comprising as it does mostly flint pebbles derived from French river valleys outside of the immediate battlezone.

The largest crater is that blown during the Battle of Messines in June 1917. In fact there were two mines in the area, one at Hill 60 and one a little farther to the south under the Caterpillar (Figure 21). Both mines were in place by October 1916, the excavation having been started in 1915, and despite German mining and counter-mining operations (34 mines were blown in this sector prior to the 1917 operation) they were detonated on June 7th 1917 with great effect, Hill 60 representing the

Itinerary I: The Ypres Salient 1914-1918

Figure 19. Destroyed Germans pillboxes (left, and right foreground) and intact British observation post (right), Hill 60.

Itinerary I: The Ypres Salient 1914-1918

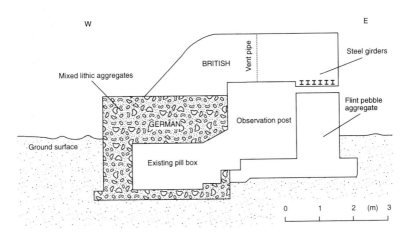

Figure 20. Sections through British observation post on Hill 60.

northerly 'hinge' of the successful advance (Figure 21). Given that the majority of the mine craters in the region are flooded today, it is perhaps surprising that those at Hill 60 are dry. Although the galleries themselves were cut through the Paniselian Formation, the crater is developed in the spoil from the railway cutting and this allows for drainage down to the more impervious Paniselian clay levels.

A number of memorials to the men who fought and were killed at Hill 60 adjoin the site (including one to the 1st Australian Tunnelling Company), and there is a bar (with toilets) in which there is housed the Queen's Westminster Rifles Museum, so called after the London territorial battalion which fought here in 1915, and who were the original owners of the site in the immediate post-war years.

Crossing the railway cutting and travelling to the T-junction with the Zillebeke road, a right turn will take you back towards Ypres (Figure 13). In travelling from Hill 60 towards Ypres the slopes of the Passchendaele Ridge are descended before reaching the clay plain. **Zillebeke Lake** is located to the right, which before the war had provided water resources for the local populace. This lake is partially fed from run - off and partially from springs at the base of the Paniselian sands. Contamination from a variety of sources was obviously a major concern during the war, although purification was attempted with varying degrees of success. Eventually a right turn (onto the N336) at another important and equally shell-swept wartime junction, **Shrapnel Corner**, will take you through the ramparts via the **Lille Gate** of the ancient walled city of Ypres or, alternatively, a left turn at the same junction will provide access via the N336 to the remainder of the itinerary in the Salient (Figure 13).

Itinerary I: The Ypres Salient 1914-1918

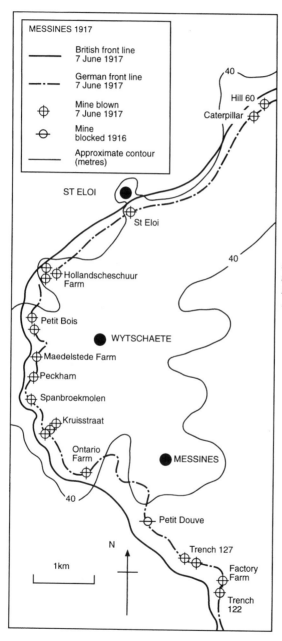

MESSINES 1917

——— British front line 7 June 1917

—·—·— German front line 7 June 1917

⊕ Mine blown 7 June 1917

⊖ Mine blocked 1916

——— Approximate contour (metres)

40

Hill 60

Caterpillar

ST ELOI

St Eloi

Hollandscheschuur Farm

40

Petit Bois

WYTSCHAETE

Maedelstede Farm

Peckham

Spanbroekmolen

Kruisstraat

Ontario Farm

MESSINES

40

Petit Douve

N

Trench 127

1km

Factory Farm

Trench 122

Figure 21. Location of mines in place for the Battle of Messines, June 1917.

Itinerary I: The Ypres Salient 1914-1918

The mine craters of Messines

Passing south through the Lille Gate from Ypres, this part of the itinerary will demonstrate the existing features of the Battle of Messines, the initial stages of which featured what is arguably the most famous use of mine warfare in the Great War (Ball, 1919; Harvey, 1929; Mullins, 1965; Pennycuick, 1965). Travelling south of Ypres on the N336 it is possible to observe on the left of the road, about 3 km from the Lille Gate, a complex of British concrete shelters at **Lankhof Farm** reputed to have had tiled hearths and other home comforts (Figure 13). These housed command and medical staff west of the front line during 1917 and are on private land, but can be clearly seen from the roadway. Close by is another red granite Demarcation Stone, situated on the right of the road, again marking the limit of the German advance in 1918. Travelling farther south the road starts to rise up the **Messines-Wytschaete Ridge,** an area which was the focus of military mining activities from 1915 up to the simultaneous explosion of nineteen mines at zero hour of the Battle of Messines on 7th June 1917 (Figure 21).

In early 1917 the British trenches were rarely at a topographic height of greater than 60 metres above sea-level, the exceptions being where the trenches cross the ridge top between Peckham and Kruisstraat. In the main, the British front line skirted around the western dip slopes of the ridge, at heights of between 50-60 metres, before descending to the clay plain. The German front line was associated with the ridge top, commanding heights greater than 70 metres at Maedelstede Farm and Spandbroekmolen. The Messines Ridge is capped by moist to dry sands overlying the Kemmel Sands which were well known to be incapable of supporting unaided either trenches or dug-outs. Both the British and German front lines were mostly cut into the sandy clays which overlie the Kemmel Sands, the German trenches being cut into the dry, well-drained Wytschaete Sands at Spandbroekmolen. British and German trenches both penetrated the Kemmel Sands on the flanks of the ridge. The Germans had the advantage in the construction of deep dug-outs, as it was possible to construct dug-outs in the clays and sands which capped the Kemmel Sands with little problem from flooding. In any case, the Germans had constructed an extensive system of surface blockhouses to combat problems with the local geology. The British, existing lower down the slopes had greater problems, although cut and cover and recess type dug-outs would be supported by the sandy clays overlying the Kemmel Sands.

The mine galleries for the Messines Offensive were all dug between 1915-1917 and were cut to considerable depths in order to penetrate the relatively dry Paniselian clays or the Ypres Clay at depth (Figure 22). These deep mines were all constructed from sap heads in the British lines and descended steeply to the clay strata. The greatest problems occurred south of Kruisstraat, where the Paniselian Formation falls away sharply to be overstepped by the moist alluvial sands of the Steenbeek valley.

Itinerary I: The Ypres Salient 1914-1918

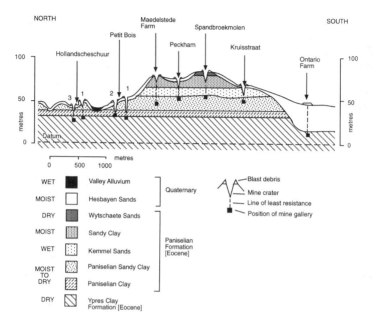

Figure 22. Geological section though the mines of the Messines-Wytschaete Ridge. Mine locations indicated on Figure 13.

Here, at Ontario Farm the galleries had to be driven though the Ypres Clay at considerable depth (Figure 22). After the opening of the Battle of Messines in June 1917 the British successfully took the ridge and assumed new positions on its eastern flanks facing Hollebeke. This was one of the most successful and carefully planned operations of the whole of the Great War and is the last time that extensive use was made of offensive mining in the war. The majority of the craters remain water-filled today, and the suggested route passes several of them. In particular those at **St Eloi, Peckham Farm,** and **Kruisstraat** should be observable from the road (Figure 13). It is possible to have a closer look at the crater developed at **Spanbroekmolen;** preserved by the Toc H movement as a memorial, and now transformed into the **Pool of Peace** (Figure 23).

Travelling south of Lankhof Farm on the N336 the St Eloi craters should be visible to the left of the road, close to the junction with the N365 (Figure 13). Galleries for these mines were cut through the Ypres Clay at a depth of approximately 40 metres, and the craters are developed in the basal clays and sandy clays of the Paniselian Formation. Continue along the N365 and upon reaching Wytschaete (Wijtschate; *'White Sheet'* to the British 'Tommies') signs to Kemmel should be followed for

Itinerary I: The Ypres Salient 1914-1918

Figure 23. 'Lone Tree' or Spanbroekmolen Crater, Messines Ridge.

about 2 km, passing on the right **Wytschaete Military Cemetery** and the adjacent monument to the 16th (Irish) Division. At this point, the Peckham Farm crater should be visible in the field, north of a small road (signposted to **Spanbroekmolen CWGC Cemetery**) on the left. Unlike the gallery for St Eloi, the gallery was dug at a depth of approximately 25 metres, and was entirely contained within the lower clay units of the Paniselian Formation. The crater is developed in the sandy clays overlying the Kemmel Sands (Figure 22). Spanbroekmolen is reached by taking the next turn on the left, a narrow road signposted to **Lone Tree Crater** (Figure 23). The crater is on the crest of the ridge and fine views can be obtained of Mont Kemmel to the east and the slopes south to Armentieres and France. Like Peckham, the galleries at Spanbroekmolen were cut through Paniselian clays at a depth of approximately 30 metres and its water-filled crater is developed in sandy clays overlying the Kemmel Sands. The dryer Wytschaete Sands cap the ridge at this point. Finally, continuing along this road for another half kilometre, signs should be followed to Wulvergem and descending down the forward slope of the Messines Ridge the twin water-filled and heavily-fished craters of Kruisstraat will be passed on the right. As with Peckham and Spanbroekmolen before them, the galleries for these mines were cut through the Paniselian clays to a depth of approximately 20 metres, but this time the craters are developed in the wet Kemmel Sands.

Other craters are present if you have the time to look for them; use of the Holts' *Battle Map of the Ypres Salient* will help you find them. At Wulvergem follow signs for Messines (Mesen), where the decision can be made to return to Ypres along the N365 or to travel on to France and Armentieres via Ploegsteert (*'Plug Street'* to the British 'Tommies'), passing on the right the impressive memorial to the missing of the campaigns in this part of France.

ITINERARY II: THE ARRAS SECTOR 1915-1917

The section of the British Front from **Lens** in the north to Arras in the south is relatively poorly known and little visited, with the notable exception of **Vimy Ridge.** The Arras sector can easily be reached by autoroute and is a convenient half-way-house between the Ypres Salient and the Somme. Visiting both of the suggested itineraries will take at least half a day, leaving ample time to visit the important battlefield site of Vimy Ridge.

The **Loos** battlefield of 1915 is situated just north of **Lens,** fairly and squarely in the heart of the Lens Coalfield. Loos was the scene of a major, but ill-fated, British offensive in 1915—the scene of the first, botched use of poison gas by the British. The **Battle of Loos** was launched in support of the French **Artois Offensive** on September 25th 1915. Although there were initial gains, the offensive failed for a variety of reasons, part of which was the lack of shells to feed the guns—a necessary part of any Great War battle dependent on artillery bombardment. In the end this battle produced no significant achievements. In travelling south to the Somme a half-day diversion can be made to examine the scene of this earlier battle.

The **Arras** battlefield of April 1917 stretches from **Lens** to Arras and includes Vimy Ridge. The battlefield can be comfortably examined over the course of a full day. In April 1917 the French launched their ill-fated offensive on the Aisne, part of a plan drawn up by the French general Nivelle who had achieved much success in the defence of Verdun in 1916. Rapidly promoted, Nivelle was a charismatic man who assured the French command that he would break the trench deadlock though the application of dramatic and intensive shock tactics backed up by artillery preparation. Nivelle was confident of its ultimate success and carried the French nation with his confidence, but ultimately the battle in April 1917 was to grind the French Army down into a state of mutiny and Nivelle was never to lead the French again. The British were more successful in support of **Nivelle's Offensive** and attacked along the front line from Arras to Vimy, on April 7th 1917, in what was to become known as the **Battle of Arras.** Gains were made through the judicious use of tunnels for the transit of troops to the front line underground and this aided in the conquest of the troublesome Vimy Ridge by the Canadian Corps, the first time the Canadians had operated as a single corps of the British Army.

The Loos battlefield

The Loos battlefield is characterised by the flat, agricultural terrain interspersed with volcanic-looking conical spoil heaps, a product of the declined coal mining industry in the region. Today, Loos is effectively a northern suburb of Lens and there are many other small mining communities which are clustered around former mine headgear (puits). If travelling south to the Somme directly from Calais using the

Itinerary II: The Arras Sector 1915-1917

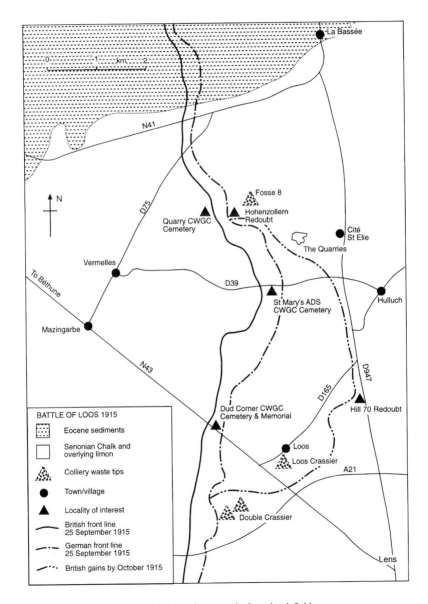

Figure 24. Locality map, the Loos battlefield.

Itinerary II: The Arras Sector 1915-1917

A26 autoroute, a detour can be made to examine part of the Loos battlefield before returning to the autoroute and travelling on to Vimy, Arras and beyond. Leaving the autoroute at Bethune *(sortie 6)*, the N41 can be followed eastwards until the junction with the N43, which should be taken south to Sailly, Mazingarbe and Lens, passing several spoil heaps. If travelling south from the Ypres Salient, the best route is to join the A25 autoroute southwest of Armentieres, following signs for Lille and joining the A1 *(sortie 1)* direction Paris. Joining the A21 autoroute *(sortie 17)* travel west to Lens and take the *Lens ouest* turn off, which will allow you to join the N43 (Figure 24).

The main focus for the diversion is **Dud Corner CWGC Cemetery**, which is situated immediately adjacent to the N43, approximately 2 km northwest of the A21, and approximately 3 km south of Mazingarbe (Figure 25). This cemetery is named after the large number of 'dud' shells which failed to explode during the battle. It is situated between the British and German front lines of September 1915 and is at the centre of the British gains, made mostly on the first day. It is actually built on a German strongpoint, called the Lens Road Redoubt by the British. Dud Corner Cemetery has a raised viewing area which can be ascended to get a good idea of the battlefield, which is remarkably flat. Geologically, the landscape is a chalk one as the coal basin, trending northwest-southeast from Douai to Bethune, is deep underground. Several chalk quarries, close to Cité St Elie, were built into the German fortifications and therefore became the focus for fighting during the battle. However, these are not visible from Dud Corner, but are present farther to the north (Figure 24).

Several other CWGC cemeteries (including **Quarry Cemetery** and **St Mary's Advanced Dressing Station Cemetery**) also lie close to the front lines of September 1915 and may be visited if time allows (Figure 24). St Mary's ADS Cemetery contains a grave of a Lieutenant of the Irish Guards which was controversially recognised and rededicated in 1992 to be that of Lieutenant John Kipling, son of Rudyard Kipling. Close by this cemetery, and south of the D39, a narrow road leads to two other CWGC cemeteries, and a number of small, dry mine craters—developed in chalk and now overgrown—can be examined adjacent to the road.

To the southwest of Dud Corner, in the far distance, it is possible to gain a view of **Vimy Ridge**. Early in the war the Germans had captured most of the Lens coalfield and the heights of Vimy Ridge which overlooked it. Possession of Vimy Ridge prevented the French and later the British from observing activities in the German lines and directing gunfire. Capturing Vimy Ridge and dominating the German-held coalfields was therefore of some importance and was the scene of several fruitless French battles in 1914-15, the enormous losses of which are commemorated by the lighthouse of **Notre Dame de Lorette.** South of the N43, and dominating the

Itinerary II: The Arras Sector 1915-1917

Figure 25. Dud Corner CWGC Cemetery, with the Double Crassier in the background, Loos Battlefield.

foreground are the twin 'peaks' of the **Double Crassier,** coal tips which are remnants of the once thriving industry of the region, the forerunners of which formed commanding features of the southern end of the Loos battlefield in 1915 (Figure 25). Other coal tips were focal points for the battle: the **Loos Crassier** (south of Loos itself) associated with complex mine head gear which was christened Tower Bridge by the troops; and **Fosse 8**, close to the formidable entrenched positions of the **Hohenzollern Redoubt** (Figure 24). Nothing much remains of these today.

Travelling southeast along the N43 and joining the A21 autoroute, signs should be followed to Arras in order to join the N17 which rises up Vimy Ridge—the fault scarp produced by the Marqueffles Fault—to the chalk upland of Artois and Arras beyond.

Canadian Memorial Park, Vimy Ridge

The **Canadian Memorial Park** at Vimy Ridge is an important stop point for any student of the battlefields of the Great War. It is well signposted from the N17 and comprises two main components, the massive twin pylons of the Canadian Memorial to the missing and the Battlefield Memorial Park, with its preserved trench lines, mine craters and tunnels from 1917 (Figure 26). Free parking and toilets are available at both locations. Picnicking is forbidden within the boundaries of the park.

Visiting the impressive Canadian Memorial first it is possible to appreciate the influence of the Marqueffles Fault in producing a prominent fault scarp, which trends to the northwest, and continues to the ridge upon which is sited the French national memorial of Notre Dame de Lorette. The tactical significance of Vimy Ridge lay in the fact the Germans, commanding the top of the ridge for much of the war (and repelling many abortive French attacks in 1915), had a significant sight advantage which allowed accurate artillery fire and reconnaissance of troop movements, providing greater protection of the Lens Coalfield below. The ridge is formed of Senonian Chalk, with Turonian Chalk cropping out at its base and in the Souchez Valley to the northwest. As with the whole of the Artois region it is mantled by a thick development of loess/loam *(limon)*. Vestiges of Landenian sands are preserved here and there, most notably at **The Pimple**—a strongpoint in the German line which was also stormed by the Canadians—and at the village of Vimy itself. The Canadian Memorial actually stands on that part of Vimy Ridge labelled on wartime maps as **Hill 145** (from its 145 metre altitude; Figure 26).

The monument itself was constructed in the 1930s, and was inaugurated by King Edward VIII in 1936 in order to mark the contribution of the Canadian forces as a whole to the Great War, fitting because it was here that the Canadian Corps first acted as one unit in the storming of the ridge in 1917. It was designed by Walter

Itinerary II: The Arras Sector 1915-1917

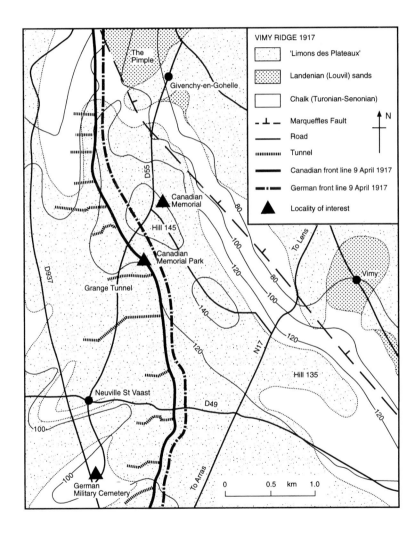

Figure 26. Vimy Ridge, location map and underground tunnels.

Itinerary II: The Arras Sector 1915-1917

Allward and commemorates the 11,285 Canadian Soldiers who were killed in France and who have no known grave; each of their names is carved around the base of the monument. The monument is constructed from Dalmatian limestone, and comprises twin pylons—reflecting the Gallic and Anglo-Saxon origins of the Canadian people—with a series of allegorical figures representing charity, faith, honour, justice and sacrifice around its top, and between them the figure of a Canadian soldier passing on a flame to his comrade. Male and female figures in grief reflect the mourning parents of Canada (Figure 27) while a lone figure facing Lens represents Canada mourning for her dead. A visitors' centre close to the memorial car park provides an explanation of the Canadian achievements at Vimy Ridge, is free to enter, and is well worth a visit.

Figure 27. The Canadian Memorial, Vimy Ridge. The Mourning Parents sculpted from Dalmatian limestone.

Close to the position of the Canadian Monument is the **Canadian Memorial Park,** a place of pilgrimage for Canadians which preserves, albeit somewhat artificially, the trench lines of early April 1917, together with part of the tunnel system constructed in Vimy Ridge open to the public during the summer months (Figure 26). The Memorial Park preserves several large mine craters which were blown by both sides during the battles from 1915-1917. The incredible thing is the close proximity of the Canadian and German trenches, a matter of a few metres. The craters, blown in the Senonian Upper Chalk (coated by the ubiquitous Quaternary *limon*) are dry and were incorporated into the front line system of both sides (Figure 28). The trenches were reconstructed in concrete during the 1930's and have lost some of their genuine feel, but they actually follow the front lines exactly as they were in 1917. The park itself is heavily shell-pocked and it is not advisable to stray off the marked paths. Each of the trees is reputed to represent a Canadian life lost in the battle.

Itinerary II: The Arras Sector 1915-1917

The Memorial Park also provides access to the **Grange Tunnel** system, a subway around 800 metres long which ran from the rear areas to the front line in order to provide access for the Canadian assault troops (Figure 26). The Grange Tunnel was one of twelve subways that were constructed over three and a half months before the attack in April 1917. They were dug at an average rate of around 4 metres per 24 hour period by five tunnelling companies, and were usually at least 6 metres deep to

Figure 28. Craters in Senonian Chalk dividing the Canadian and German front lines, Vimy Ridge.

prevent penetration from large calibre howitzer shell fire. As infantry subways they were two metres high and approximately a metre wide, and were furnished with electrical light (Figure 29). Some also had tramways fitted to allow for stores to be transported to the front. Water supply was gained by tapping the water table which was at depth in the Senonian Chalk and which fluctuated in height throughout the year. In addition to the infantry subways, eight offensive mines were also laid under the German front line; only two of those were blown, and the remainder have lain under the ridge ever since: Lt Col. Mike Watkins, a bomb disposal expert, was tragically killed by a rockfall exploring for these mine tunnels in August 1998.

The Grange Tunnel was reopened to the public in the late 1980's with the aid of the Royal Engineers, as reported in the *Proceedings of the Geologists' Association* by Rosenbaum (1989). Access is in groups led by Canadian guides and a tour of the tunnel is dependent on the number of people there. Tours generally commence at 10.00 am and are free of charge. Cut through the Senonian Upper Chalk it is possible to observe the dryness of the tunnels and the construction of a number of chambers which housed command and medical staff, amongst others. Flint lines are clearly visible, as are the regularly spaced channels cut in the walls in order to take

Itinerary II: The Arras Sector 1915-1917

Figure 29. Grange Tunnel, cut thought Senonian Chalk. Left, the widest part of the subway system, the wooden pit-props replaced by concrete ones; right, original electrical insulators.

Itinerary II: The Arras Sector 1915-1917

the wooden pit props intended to give extra support to the roof (Figure 29). This tunnel, and others like it still under Vimy Ridge, gave the tactical advantage to the allies and provided for the early successes of the Battle of Arras as it allowed troops to reach the front by underground means, providing almost total protection from hostile shellfire.

Arras

The city of Arras is a convenient place to stay in northern France, and its position close to the intersection of the A1 and A26 autoroutes means that it provides good access to the Somme battlefields farther to the south, as well as being easily accessible direct from Calais.

Importantly, Arras has been famous for its underground tunnels and chambers, dug deep into the Chalk since medieval times. Many of the chambers having been a

Figure 30. La Grand Place Arras. The buildings (left), are partially faced with sarsen stone and with chalk excavated from underground chambers, and the streets are paved with sarsen cobbles (right).

source of building stone which can be seen in some of the facings of the ancient buildings in the justly famous **Grand Place** (Figure 30). The underground car park of the Grand Place is actually located within one such chamber. During the war Arras was an important centre for the British Army and the tunnels, sewers and chambers were linked and extended by mostly New Zealand Tunnelling Companies to provide shelter from bombardment, and access for assault troops to the British front line, which was alarmingly close to the west and southwest of the city (Figure 31). As with the assault on Vimy Ridge, the use of these tunnels provided an advantage to the sheltering troops and overall the line was pushed forwards a few kilometres. Accomodation for around 11,000 men was provided in this way. The entrance to the tunnels *(boves)* is actually in the square next to the Grand Place, close to the **Hotel de Ville,** and access is possible at limited opening times, usually Saturday mornings and Sunday afternoons

Travelling south from Arras along the N17, signposted to Beaurains and Bapaume, provides access to the Somme Battlefield of 1916 and the remainder of the itinerary.

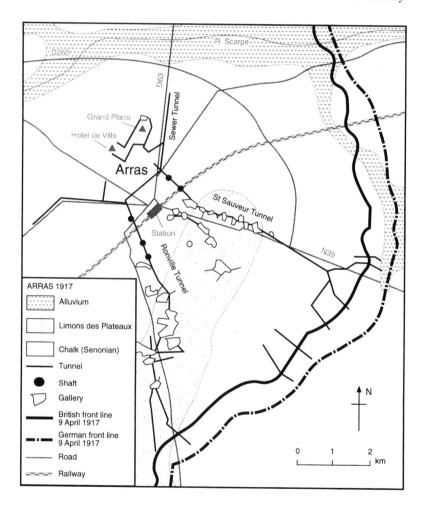

Figure 31. Arras, location of major tunnel systems used in 1917.

ITINERARY III: THE SOMME BATTLEFIELD 1916

The **Battle of the Somme** (July-November 1916) was to become primarily a British offensive, although it was initially planned as a Franco-British 'push' to take place at the junction of the two armies, in the Somme region. Latterly, its importance was as a diversion to draw German troops and resources away from the **Battle of Verdun** being waged to the east, but even so, General Haig was confident that the battle could result in a break through of the German line and confidently predicted a 'walk over' following the massive artillery bombardment which preceded it. The battle was opened on a front of 29 kilometres north of the River Somme, from Maricourt in the south to Gommecourt in the north (Figure 32). In addition, the French were to attack to the south of Maricourt and the Somme River. The German positions were mostly established on high ground and were well constructed, a particular feature being deep dug-outs cut in chalk, a factor which is often cited as a major influence in the failure of the British to make headway on the opening day.

The itinerary proposed examines the battlefront from Serre and Beaumont Hamel to Thiepval in the centre of the British attack, before going on to visit the Lochnagar mine crater at La Boisselle. It will take at least a day and it is important to note that bars and other hostelries are relatively few and far between in the area. The most important access route is via the D929 Amiens-Albert-Bapaume road, a former straight Roman road which bisects the Maricourt-Gommecourt front line of 1916. This can be reached directly from the A1 autoroute (*sortie* 15, Bapaume) or by the N17 via Beaurains from Arras. An alternative route is to take the D919 (via Achicourt), which will take you to Puisieux and Serre and the commencement of the itinerary. However, it is of course possible using maps for the region—the Michelin 236 will suffice—to visit the sites suggested in any order, and in your own time.

Serre

Travelling southwest from Arras the rolling chalk landscape of the Artois region is crossed: the Somme battlefield of 1916, a name which still has a great resonance to us eighty or more years on and to which increasing numbers of visitors come every year. Travelling southwest on the D919 **Puisieux** is passed through, close to the German second line of defence in 1916, and the German and British front lines are crossed near **Serre** (Figure 33). Close by, on the plateau top, a fraction of the British front line is preserved in the **Sheffield Memorial Park** (Figure 33—location 1) and the Serre road has several large concentration cemeteries marking the intense struggles in the area (Figure 33—location 2).

The Sheffield Memorial Park is located on the plateau top of what is effectively an anticlinal structure, one of the northwest-southeast trending flexures of the gently folded chalk upland that has so affected the drainage pattern. It is reached by an

Itinerary III: The Somme Battlefield 1916

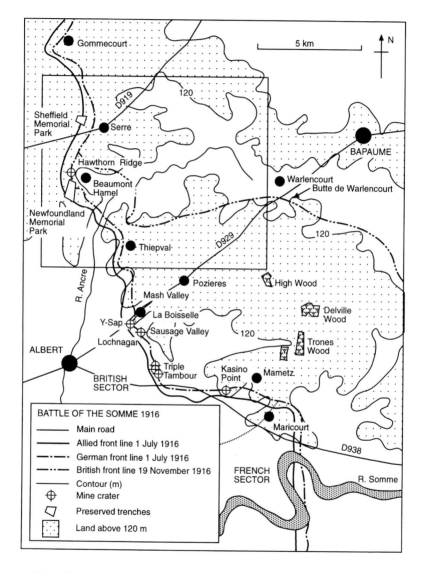

Figure 32. The Somme Battlefield, 1916. The outline box denotes the area of Figure 33.

access track north of the D919 signposted to **Luke Copse, Railway Hollow, Queens'** and **Serre Road No 3 CWGC cemeteries.** Approximately 100 metres farther west along the D919, the major concentration cemeteries of **Serre Road No 1**; and the **French National Cemetery Serre-Hébuterne** are reached, and farther west still **Serre Road No 3** (on the site of the German fortification known as the Quadrilateral). The access track to the Memorial Park, and the four CWGC cemeteries situated along it, follow the front line of 1916 and the park itself preserves a fragment of the British line, now grassed over and wooded. It was adopted by Sheffield after the war, as it was here that many men of its 'pals' battalion—friends and colleagues from Sheffield (and also Accrington) who joined the army in the early parts of the war and who served together on the Somme as the Sheffield City Battalion were effectively sacrificed in the opening minutes of the battle. The British were attacking along a spur of the chalk plateau and their trenches were cut into the *limon* complex which mantles the whole of the chalk plateaux of the region.

Rejoining the D919 and continuing westwards past the concentration cemeteries, the next left turn should be taken which eventually joins the D53 to **Beaumont Hamel** (Figure 32).

The 'Sunken lane' and Hawthorn Ridge mine crater, Beaumont Hamel

Beaumont Hamel is situated on the flanks of a chalk plateau which is capped by the usual mantle of loess/loam *(limons des plateaux)* and clay-with-flints, and dissected by the northeast—southwest flowing River Ancre. Serre is situated on the same plateau to the northeast, separated from Beaumont Hamel by a narrow spur, the Redan Ridge. Like Serre, Beaumont Hamel was close to the northern end of the main Somme batttlefront and its capture was one of the objectives of the first day of the battle on 1st July 1916, the intention being to advance beyond the village to the German second line. The village of **Thiepval** was also an objective of the first day of the Somme and is located to the southeast of Beaumont, on the opposite flanks of the incised Ancre valley, but again situated on the same northwest-southeast trending flexure as Beaumont Hamel and Serre (Figure 33).

A number of dry valleys dissect the chalk plateau, several of them trending northwest-southeast and opening into the main valley of the Ancre. Usually the dry valleys in this chalk country are a consequence of deep ground freezing (periglacial permafrost) activity during the last Ice Age. During it, with the upper levels of the chalk frozen, there was very little movement of sub-surface ground water. Any flow of water was predominantly on the surface and it was this flow which eventually initiated or enlarged pre-exisiting valleys. As the Ice Age came to a close sub - surface water flow progressively resumed, water tables in the Chalk fell and the

Itinerary III: The Somme Battlefield 1916

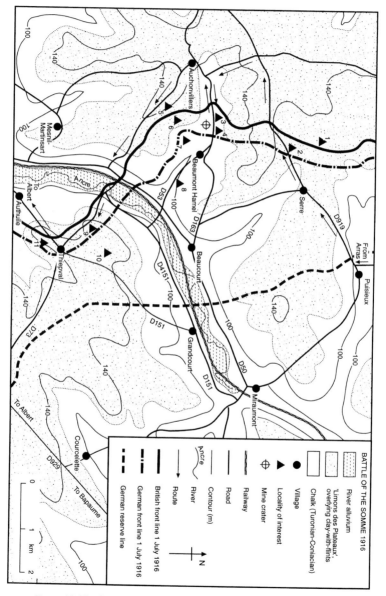

Figure 33. The Somme, locality map (numbers referred to in text) and route.

Itinerary III: The Somme Battlefield 1916

valleys became dry, although many to this day are affected by seasonal surface flow from springs, as in the Guilotte valley, close to Beaucourt. Beaumont Hamel is situated on the northeastern flank of one of these dry valleys, the Beaumont valley. A most striking feature of this particular one is the **Y-Ravine** *(Ravin en Y)*, which forms a deeply incised tributary, and which will be examined in detail in the **Newfoundland Memorial Park**. A less incised tributary parallels the Y-Ravine to the north and this is followed by the main Beaumont–Auchonvillers road. These tributaries divide the flanks of the opposing plateau into spurs, two important ones being the **Redan Ridge,** north of the Beaumont-Auchonvillers Road, and **Hawthorn Ridge**, south of this road (Figure 33). Other roads in the area are characteristically incised as 'sunken roads' into the plateau. Like the sunken roads in Kent, these developed due to the use of iron-shod wheeled traffic which wore down the tracks on chalk and Quaternary sediments alike, to form incised roadways. These became important as improvised trenches during the Great War.

The British front line of early 1916 in this area was restricted to the southeastern flanks of the Beaumont valley, and descended down to the Ancre River. The trenches were situated on a 'forward slope' and as such presumably had artillery observation in the rear, on the highest ground. A salient was formed where the line skirted around the head of the Y-Ravine and then closely followed the spur formed between the ravine and the small dry valley to the south. The German front line was situated on the lower flanks of the same side of the Beaumont valley, closely following the form of the Y-Ravine. A heavily defended strong point, the **Hawthorn Redoubt,** was developed at the foot of the Hawthorn Ridge.

Driving along the D53 to Beaumont Hamel it is possible to observe that part of the British line which crosses the Beaumont-Auchonvillers road, situated in the dry valley between Redan Ridge to the north and Hawthorn Ridge to the south. This area is historically interesting because it is from here, close to an area known as **White City** to the troops (because of the shell-blasted and exposed chalk of the region), and at the top of a stepped communication trench known as **Jacob's Ladder,** that the cinematographer Geoffrey Malins filmed Lancashire Fusiliers of the 29th Division in the front line (Figure 34). Importantly, Malins also captured the explosion of a mine under the Hawthorn Redoubt at 7.20 am on 1st July 1916, during the making of his film *The Battle of the Somme.* The location is signposted **Beaumont Hamel CWGC Cemetery** on the left of the road and a small parking area is provided at the foot of a Celtic cross memorial to the Argyll and Sutherland Highlanders. The **Sunken Lane** (Figure 33—location 3), which is entered from this point, is a typically incised chalk country lane which was in No Man's Land; this served as a 'jumping off' trench for the Lancashire Fusiliers on the 1st July. Recent earth movements have uncovered 'funkhole' dug-outs (Figure 35). The Sunken Lane can clearly be identified in Geoffrey Malins' film. Beaumont Hamel CWGC Cemetery (Figure 33—location 4), just east of the Sunken Lane, and marking the

Itinerary III: The Somme Battlefield 1916

Figure 34. Lancashire Fusiliers at the White City, 1st July 1916; a still from Geoffrey Malins'
film. Reproduced with permission of the Trustees of the Imperial War Museum,
negative no. Q744.

position of the German barbed wire, contains several 1st July casualties, all of whom
were buried many months after the battle.

Cross the road and walk up the the valley to Hawthorn Ridge where the Hawthorn
Ridge mine crater can be examined (Figures 33, 36, 37 and rear cover). This is
signposted and is reached by a series of steps. It is possible, with care, to gain
access to the bottom of the crater, although this can be slippery and old munitions
can be found lying around remnants of this and later Somme battles. The crater
exposes the Chalk in its bottom, but is suffering mass slippage around its rim
developed in the *limon* complex, which caps the chalk plateau. In his famous book
The Old Front Line, published in 1917, John Masefield described the form of this
crater, which clearly picks out the depth of the *limon* overlying the Chalk: 'It is like
the crater of a volcano, vast, ragged and irregular, about one hundred and fifty yards
long, one hundred yards across, and twenty-five yards deep. It is crusted and
scabbed with yellowish tetter, like sulphur or the rancid fat on meat. The inside has
rather the look of meat, for it is reddish and all streaked and scabbed with this pox
and with discoloured chalk.'

Itinerary III: The Somme Battlefield 1916

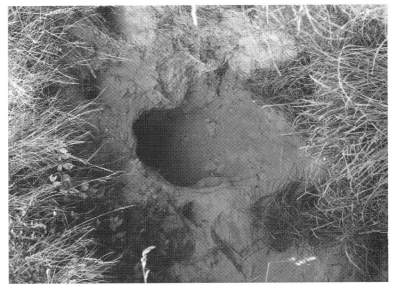

Figure 35. The Sunken Lane, Beaumont Hamel; the lane (right) and exposed 'funk hole' dug-out (left)

Itinerary III: The Somme Battlefield 1916

Figure 36. Hawthorn Ridge Mine and crater, exploded at 7.20 a.m on 1st July 1916. Right, the crater as it is today. Left, the mine exploding at 7.20, as filmed by Geoffrey Malins from the White City. Reproduced with permission of the Trustees of the Imperial War Museum, Negative no. Q754.

The mine was dug by the 252nd Tunnelling Company R.E., and was blown ten minutes before zero hour, at 7.20 a.m., and before the other mines on the Somme were blown (Figure 36). Geoffrey Malins captured this on film from the White City, and this image is one of the most dramatic to survive from the Great War (Figure

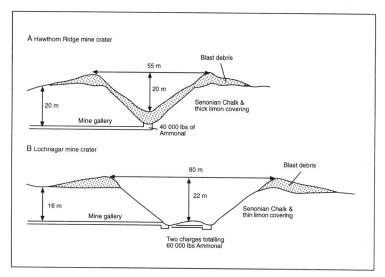

Figure 37. Mines blown on the Somme, 1st July 1916

36). The early explosion of the mine was the result of a decision made by General Hunter-Weston, the Corps Commander for this area, who believed it would provide an advantage. In fact, it only served to prepare the Germans for the imminent attack ten minutes later; the crater was not captured until much later in the battle.

If the flint-bearing Senonian Chalk of the region is to be examined, continue eastwards along the D53 to Beaumont and beyond. The Chalk is exposed in a road-side quarry, and here it is possible to examine the regular lines of flints and the frost-shattered upper part of the Chalk (Figure 9; Figure 33—location 8). The D53 runs along a dry valley and it is possible also to see incised terraces of *limon* on the south side of the valley. Double back westwards long the D53 to Auchonvilliers to continue with the rest of the itinerary.

Newfoundland Memorial Park, Beaumont Hamel

Returning west along the D53 Beaumont–Auchonvilliers road, at Auchonvilliers (*'Ocean Villas'* to the British Tommies), take a left turn on to the D73 signposted to the Newfoundland Memorial Park (Figure 33). This road, named St John's Road after the Newfoundland capital, runs parallel to Hawthorn Ridge and provides access to the park and the memorials of Thiepval beyond (Figures 33, 38). Like the Sheffield example, the Newfoundland Memorial Park is an area of trenches from the 1916 battle which has been preserved intact by the Canadian authorities, this time without concrete enhancement. There is a small parking area, but no other facilities. Lately, Canadian student guides have been on hand during the summer months to help visitors' orientation and understanding of the site.

The area of the park is actually the site of the attack at zero hour by the British 29th Division (which included the Lancashire Fusiliers), but it is preserved in honour of the sacrifice of the men of the Royal Newfoundland Regiment. During the battle the Newfoundlanders were brought in from the third line and were mown down by the German machine gunners whilst crossing the open ground from reserve to forward trench positions, the result of a hopelessly clogged communication trench. Out of 801 men who entered the battle, only 68 survived without wounds—the highest casualty rate of any unit on the Somme. A baying caribou (actually one of three on the Western Front) constructed on a granite mound commemorates this action and all Newfoundlanders who died in the war.

The British front line trenches (Figure 33—location 5; Figure 38) occupied the high ground here and were founded in the *limon,* a factor which militated against the comfort of their occupants in the later, winter phases of the battle. Moving northeastwards down the slope, in the manner of the troops on the day, it is possible to pick out in slope morphology the transition from the *limon* to the Chalk (Figure 39), and this is about as far as the British were able to advance through the murderous fire produced from the German positions at its base. Another trench, this

Itinerary III: The Somme Battlefield 1916

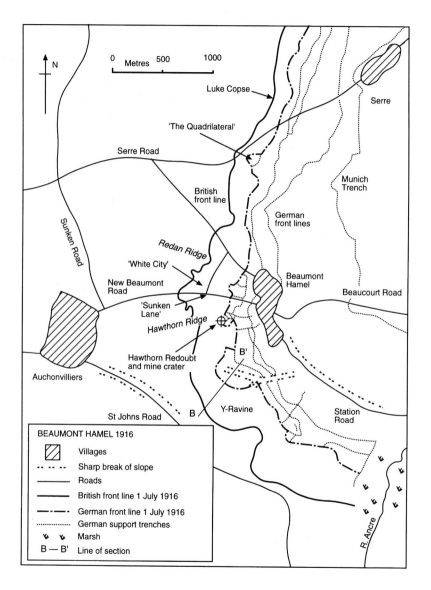

Figure 38. Sketch map of the area surrounding the Newfoundland Memorial Park, Beaumont Hamel.

Itinerary III: The Somme Battlefield 1916

one an attempt much later in 1916 to advance the British line by joining shell holes at night, can also be seen. Eventually, the German front line is reached, and behind it **Y-Ravine** (Figure 33—location 7). The German front line was located around the fortified ruins of the village of Beaumont Hamel and incorporated Y-Ravine into its defences (Figures 38, 40). Extensive tunnels and dug-outs, an underground maze, were constructed into the north-facing slope of the ravine and as such were impenetrable to British shell fire, which was directed from behind the battlefront and therefore had a very poor line of sight. As John Masefield reported in 1917: 'Whenever the enemy has had a bank of any kind, at all screened from fire, he has dug into it for shelter. In the Y-Ravine, which provided these great expanses of banks, he dug himself shelters of unusual strength and size. He sank shafts into the banks, tunnelled long living rooms, linked the rooms together with galleries, and cut hatchways and bolting holes to lead to the surface as well as the gully. All this work was securely done, with baulks of seasoned wood, iron girders, and concreting.' Incorporating the Y-Ravine into the front line was an extremely effective use of the natural topography and distinctive features of the Chalk landscape. Because of this, Beaumont Hamel was not captured until November 1916 and its consolidation by the 51st Highland Division (also commemorated here) was a considerable feat accomplished only on the last official day of the battle, November 19th, 1916. Several CWGC cemeteries and memorials commemorate the dead of the momentous struggles which took place in this area in 1916.

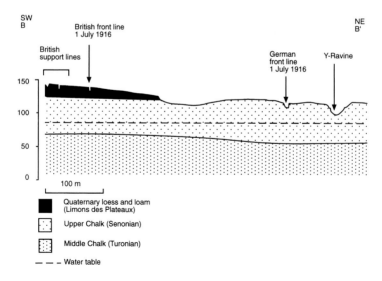

Figure 39. Sketch geological section, Newfoundland Memorial Park. Approximate line of section (B-B') denoted on figure 38.

Itinerary III: The Somme Battlefield 1916

Figure 40. Newfoundland Memorial Park: the German lines (top) and Y- Ravine (bottom).

Itinerary III: The Somme Battlefield 1916

Leaving the park and continuing southeastwards along the St John's Road, it is possible to get a view of the Thiepval Memorial on the other side of the Ancre River valley, and constructed on the plateau top, a continuation of the Chalk anticlinal flexure that has been followed from Serre. St John's Road is incised in the manner of the sunken roads of the region and it is possible to gain an impression of the thickness of the *limon* complex which mantles the plateaux of the Somme. The road more-or-less parallels the front line of 1916 (Figure 33). Upon reaching the village of Hamel in the Ancre valley follow the signs for the 36th (Ulster) Division (Figure 33—location 9) and Thiepval memorials (Figure 33—location 11) to the left, and cross the railway and river on to the D73 which rises up the valley side opposite.

Ulster Tower and the Thiepval Memorial

Ascending onto the plateau a memorial tower, the **Ulster Tower**, is reached (Figure 33—location 9). This memorial has a parking area and a small visitors' centre, including a museum, small cafe and toilets, which is open most of the year, with the exception of December and January. The tower is a replica of the Helen's Tower which stands on the estate of the Marquis of Dufferin and Ava in County Down. It commemorates the action of the 36th (Ulster) Division in the storming the German line on 1st July and in capturing the fortified position known as the **Schwaben Redoubt** (Figure 33—location 10), now the location of **Mill Road CWGC Cemetery,** situated to the rear of the tower on the plateau top. This cemetery is unusual, as the headstones are all laid flat—reportedly a function of the unstable ground provided by the extensive dug-outs and underground shelters of the Redoubt. The German lines here dominated the plateau top, with the British at the disadvantage, having once more to advance up the slope in the face of German fire. Men of the Ulster Division were the only soldiers north of the Amiens-Bapaume Road to actually pierce the German lines on the first day and as they were in advance of all other British units they were shelled by their own artillery. Across the road from the Tower is another larger cemetery, **Connaught CWGC Cemetery,** with many Ulster men and farther east along it, the **Thiepval Memorial**, situated to the right on the D151.

The area of the plateau top has a thick development of *limon*. The mixture of permeable and impermeable units in this complex mantling the Senonian Chalk contributed to problems later in the Somme campaign, particularly so as tanks were used in order to capture Thiepval. John Masefield described it in early 1917: 'The mud of the Somme, which will be remembered by our soldiers long after they have forgotten the shelling, was worse at Thiepval than elsewhere, or, at least, could not have been worse elsewhere. The road through Thiepval was a bog, the village was a quagmire. Near the chateau there were bits where one sank to the knee. In the great battle for Thiepval, on the 26th of last September, one of our Tanks charged an enemy trench here. It plunged and stuck fast and remained in the mud, like a great

Itinerary III: The Somme Battlefield 1916

Figure 41. Mud on the Somme. An Australian officer struggles though a communication trench cut in the limon near Guedecourt. Reproduced with permission of the Trustees of the Imperial War Museum, negative no. E (AUS) 572.

animal stricken dead in its spring.' Other parts of the Somme battlefield were also to suffer severe problems with the winter mud (Figure 41).

Thiepval village was situated on the plateau top and the **Thiepval Memorial to the Missing of the Somme** (Figure 33—location 11), was built here in a commanding position. It is a nationally important monument, the Somme equivalent of the Menin Gate in the Ypres Salient. Unveiled in 1932, and designed by Sir Edwin Lutyens, this impressive memorial names all those who were killed in the Somme battles and who have no known grave. It was built on extensive rafted foundations, a function of the amount of tunnels and dug-outs constructed in the region during the war.

Itinerary III: The Somme Battlefield 1916

Beyond it is a joint British and French cemetery commemorating the action of both nations in the battle.

From the Thiepval Memorial continue southwestwards along the D151, passing the **Autheille** and **Blighty Valley CWGC Cemeteries,** for around 3.5 kilometres until the junction with the D20 to La Boisselle is reached (Figure 33). Take the D20 upon joining the main D929 Amiens-Bapaume road, at **La Boisselle,** cross straight over and follow the distinctive brown signs with poppy motif labelled *La Grande Mine.*

Lochnagar mine crater, La Boisselle

The last stop will be to examine the largest mine crater on the Somme, that at La Boisselle which was known as **Lochnagar** (Figures 32, 37, 42). This has been preserved as a memorial to the dead of both sides and its sheer scale is a testimony to the fact that two separate explosive charges were used. Unlike Hawthorn Ridge this mine was exploded precisely at zero hour, 7.30 a.m., on the 1st July 1916. It is developed in Senonian Chalk, with only a thin covering of *limon* and contemporary illustrations show it gleaming in the sunlight. In this way it is distinctly different from the Hawthorn Ridge mine, which was in any case blown using a single charge (Figure 37). It is conceivable that this was the crater captured on Geoffrey Malins' film, intending to represent the Hawthorn Ridge crater (which was of course still in enemy hands at the time). Both the Hawthorn Ridge and Lochnagar mine craters, in common with others blown for the Somme battle, are dry and this is in direct contrast with those examined at Messines (Figure 23 & 42). Interestingly, many of the Messines mines were blown with greater amounts of ammonal explosives, but have smaller craters. This is clearly a function of the distinctly different lithologies involved; the clay and sands of the Messines mines falling back into the mine crater; the more brittle chalk having been mostly expelled from the Somme craters to form

Figure 42. View from the bottom of Lochnagar Crater, La Boisselle. This crater is developed in Senonian Chalk with only a thin limon covering.

Itinerary III: The Somme Battlefield 1916

a debris apron (Figure 37).

Having examined this crater return to the D929. A choice can be made to return northeast to the A1 autoroute via Bapaume, crossing the whole area of the battlefield and several memorials and important battlesites; or to visit the town of Albert, a focus for British activity during the war, similar in this respect to Ypres and Arras. If returning to Bapaume, the progress of the Somme battle in 1916 may be followed, thanks to the brown roadside orientation signs which pick out the line of the front at successive stages. The final line of the 1916 battle is reached at the **Butte de Warlencourt,** a tree-covered ancient burial mound which marks the limit of the British advance in 1916 and which was the scene of hard fighting during late 1916 (Figure 23 & 43). Other road-side memorials include the Australian memorial at **Pozieres,** and the distinctive Tank Corps memorial at **Courcellete.** Study of the Holts' *Battlefield Map of the Somme* will repay the visitor who wishes to explore these and other features of the Somme Battlefield.

Figure 43. The Butte de Warlencourt; an ancient burial mound (centre right) at the limit of the British advance during the last stages of the Battle of the Somme in November 1916.

Albert

Albert is a northern French town with an industrial feel which was an entry point for British troops to the Somme battlefield and which was extensively damaged during the war. It is most famous for its **Basilica of the Golden Virgin**, another post-war reconstruction based on an original (Figure 14). Like the Cloth Hall in Ypres, this church was a famous landmark during the war years and was badly damaged. Its toppled golden statue of the Virgin Mary and Child developed legendary status, as some considered that when the statue fell from the tower the war would end. In fact, the tower and its statue were blown up by British engineers in April 1918 in order to prevent it being used as an observation post during the German advance. Albert has some bars and food shops, and has a pleasant public park. Car parking is available on street and in the square. Albert also hosts the *Musée des Abris,* a war museum set

Itinerary III: The Somme Battlefield 1916

in underground shelters dating from just before the Second World War which is worth a visit. An entry fee is payable.

Returning along the D929 the A1 autoroute can be reached. Visitors with extra time may want to visit other sites in the Somme region, particularly those south of the Amiens-Bapaume road. Important locations include Mametz and the South African memorial park at **Delville Wood,** near Longueval (which has a visitors centre, museum, cafe and toilets), and the important battlefield sites of High and Trones Woods (Figure 32). The Somme battlefield is dotted with CWGC cemeteries, isolated memorials and relics of trenches; exploration with a good guide book and an adequate map will well repay the inquisitive.

Geology of the Western Front, 1914 - 1918

CONCLUDING REMARKS

From the itineraries discussed and sites visited it can be seen that geology had a significant impact on the outcome of the Great War on the Western Front. In fact, many of the failed offensives and human suffering of the Western Front can be traced to an insufficient understanding of the nature of the underlying geology. This is particularly the case in the Passchendaele Offensive which followed the Battle of Messines in Autumn 1917. Here, an intense bombardment led to the creation of an extensively cratered landscape in the Palaeogene clays which was incapable of draining surface waters, and which was to be the graveyard of both men and machines; it is well known that tanks quickly became ineffective here, hopelessly bogged down in this quagmire.

However, the British Army, through its small establishment of geologists attached to the Royal Engineers, did have a good understanding of the importance of geology to the waging of this static war, particularly where it came to the adequate provision of potable water, and in the construction of defensive positions. Despite this, more often than not, the siting of these positions was more usually dictated by tactical expediency and strategic policy rather than the best use of ground. This is clearly demonstrated by the situation at Beaumont Hamel, where incorporation of naturally strong geological features into trench systems made them almost impregnable.

It is clear from the lessons of the Great War that a sufficient understanding of geology is important in order to gain tactical advantages. Although this lesson has been learnt, in many cases it has been neglected. In open as well as static warfare, the best possible information about ground conditions and geology should be collated from all sources. Hopefully the field excursions suggested in this guide will help the casual reader and visitor alike to appreciate the importance of geology in any armed conflict, and to understand how its inadequate exploration directly contributed to the misery of those men who struggled to exist on the Western Front some eighty years or more ago.

SELECTED FURTHER READING

Guides and histories

BATTLEGROUND EUROPE. A series of books published by Pen & Sword Books, and written by several authors, which are regularly updated and added to, and which provide details of the whole of the Western Front.

BROWN, M. 1993. *The Imperial War Museum Book of the Western Front.* Sidgwick & Jackson, London, 274pp. [Aspects of life on the Western Front based on archival material].

COOMBS, R.E.B. 1990. *Before endeavours fade. A guide to the battlefields of the First World War.* Sixth edition. After the Battle Publications, London, 164pp. [Comprehensive guide to all battlefields of the Western Front].

HOLT, T. & HOLT, V. 1993. *Battlefields of the First World War. A Traveller's Guide.* Pavillion Books, London, 186pp. [Useful single volume guide to all major areas of the Western Front].

HOLT, T. & HOLT, V. 1996. *Major & Mrs Holt's battlefield guide to the Somme.* Leo Cooper, London, 254pp [Well-illustrated, informative guide; comes with a separate fold-out map].

HOLT, T. & HOLT, V. 1997. *Major & Mrs Holt's battlefield guide to the Ypres Salient.* Leo Cooper, London, 256pp [Well-illustrated, informative guide; comes with a separate fold-out map].

JOHNSON, J.H. 1995. *Stalemate! The great trench warfare battles of 1915-1917.* Arms & Armour Press, London, 224pp. [Overview of the main battles discussed in this guide, including Loos, Ypres, Somme and Arras].

MACDONALD, L. 1993a. *They called it Passchendaele.* Penguin Books, Harmondsworth, 253pp. [Popular account by a respected author].

MACDONALD, L. 1993b. *Somme.* Penguin Books, Harmondsworth, 366pp. [Popular account by a respected author].

MASEFIELD, J. 1917. *The old front line.* William Heinemann, London, 128 pp. [Contemporary topographical account of the British front line in the Battle of the Somme].

MIDDLEBROOK, M. 1971. *The first day on the Somme.* Allen Lane, Harmondsworth, 365pp. [Modern classic on the Somme].

MIDDLEBROOK, M. & MIDDLEBROOK, M. 1994. *The Somme battlefields.* Penguin Books, Harmondsworth, 385 pp. [Nicely written account].

OLDHAM, P. 1995. *Pill boxes on the Western Front.* Leo Cooper, London, 208pp. [Account of concrete structures; discusses the diplomatic problems of imported aggregates and concrete].

SMITHER, R. (Ed.) 1993. *The Battles of the Somme and Ancre.* Imperial War Museum and DD Video, 58 pp. [Comprehensive guide to Geoffrey Malins' contemporary films; accompanies the video of the same name].

Selected further reading

General geology

DELATTRE, C., MERIAUX, E. & WATERLOT, M. 1973. *Région du Nord.*
Flandre, Artois, Boulonnais, Picardie. Guides Géologiques Régionaux, Masson,
Paris, 176 pp. [Useful field guide & summary].
POMEROL, C. 1980. *Geology of France.* Guides Géologiques Régionaux, Masson,
Paris, 256pp. [Brief, English language overview].
POMEROL, C. 1982. *The Cenozoic Era. Tertiary and Quaternary.* Ellis Horwood
Ltd, Chichester. [Extremely useful overview, with sections on Palaeogene and
Quaternary deposits of France and Flanders].
PROUVOST, J. (Ed.) 1969. Geologie du nord de la France. *Annales de la Societe
Geologique de la France,* **89,** 129pp. [Important collection of papers, still often cited].
ROBASZYNSKI, F. & DUPUIS, C. 1983. *Belgique.* Guides Géologiques
Régionaux, Masson, Paris, 204 pp. [Useful field guide & summary].
STAMP, L.D. 1919. Note sur la Geologie du Mont Aigu et du Mont Kemmel.
Annales de la Societe Geologique de la France, **46,** 115-126. [Details of the
Palaeogene successions of these Flanders hills).
STAMP, L.D. 1921a. On cycles of sedimentation in the Eocene strata of the Anglo-
Franco-Belgian Basin. *Geological Magazine,* **58,** 108-114, 146-157, 194-200.
[Seminal work stemming from his military service].
STAMP, L.D. 1921b. On the beds at the base of the Ypresian (London Clay) in the
Anglo-Franco-Belgian Basin. *Proceedings of the Geologists' Association,* **32,** 57-
108. [Still useful explanation of the Palaeogene sediments].
STAMP, L.D. 1922. Long excursion to Belgium. *Proceedings of the Geologists'
Association,* **33,** 39-74. [Early field guide].
STAMP, L.D., MAILLEUX, M.E., DELEPINE, G., PRUVOST, P. & CORNET, J.
1922. The Geology of Belgium. *Proceedings of the Geologists' Association,* **33,** 1-
38. [Early general account].

Geology and the Great War.

BROOKS, A.H. 1920. The use of geology on the Western Front. *United States
Geological Survey Professional Papers,* **128-D,** 85-124. [Important, often quoted
work from one of the American military geologists].
DOYLE, P. & BENNETT, M.R. 1997a. Military geography: terrain evaluation and
the British Western Front, 1914-1918. *Geographical Journal,* **163,** 1-24. [Recent
publication on the geology and topography of the Western Front].
DOYLE, P. & BENNETT, M.R. 1997b. Geology on the Western Front, 1914-1918.
Stand To! The Journal of the Western Front Association, **49,** 34-38. [Recent
publication on importance of geology on the Western Front]
INSTITUTION OF ROYAL ENGINEERS. 1921. *The work of the Royal Engineers
in the European War, 1914-19: water supply.* W. & J. Mackay, Chatham, 54pp.

Selected further reading

[R.E. official account].

INSTITUTION OF ROYAL ENGINEERS. 1922a. *The work of the Royal Engineers in the European War, 1914-19: geological work on the Western Front.* Institution of Royal Engineers, Chatham, 71pp. [R.E. official account].

JOHNSON, D.W. 1921. *Battlefields of the World War, Western and Southern fronts: a study of military geography.* American Geographical Society Research Series 3, Oxford University Press, New York, 648pp. [Interesting topographical account by one of the American military geologists].

KING, W.B.R. 1919. Geological work on the Western Front. *Geographical Journal,* **54,** 201-221. [Account of the work of Captain King].

KING, W.B.R. 1921a. Résultats des sondages exécutés par les armées britanniques dans la Nord de la France. *Annales de la Société géologique du Nord,* **45,** 9-26. [Results of the water supply explorations by Captain King].

KING, W.B.R. 1921b. The surface of the marls of the Middle Chalk in the Somme Valley and the neighbouring districts of northern France, and the effect on the hydrology. *Quarterly Journal of the Geological Society of London,* **77,** 135-143. [Results of the water supply explorations by King himself].

SABINE, P.A. 1991. Geologists at war: a forensic investigation in the field of war-time diplomacy. *Proceedings of the Geologists' Association,* **102,** 139-143. [Discussion of the origin of aggregates used in German pillboxes].

STRAHAN, A. 1917. Geology at the seat of war. *Geological Magazine,* **64,** 68-74. [Geology of the battlefields by the head of the Geological Survey].

Military mining on the Western Front.

BALL, H.S. 1919. The work of the miner on the Western Front 1915-1918. *Transactions of the Institute of Mining and Metallurgy,* **28,** 189-248, pl. 3-22. [Excellent summary with coloured section of the Messines Ridge].

BARRIE, A. 1988. *War underground. The tunnellers of the Great War.* Tom Donovan, London. [An interesting if anecdotal account of the activities of the Royal Engineers Tunnelling Companies].

BRANAGAN, D. 1987. The Australian Mining Corps in World War 1. *Bulletin and Proceedings of the Australian Institute of Mining and Metallurgy,* **292,** 40-44. [Account of Australian mining corps on the Western Front].

HAMMOND, B. 1991. Professionals and specialists: military mining on the Western Front. *Imperial War Museum Review,* **6,** 4-15. [IWM account].

HARVEY, R.N. 1929. Military mining in the Great War. *Royal Engineers Journal,* **43,** 537-548. [Account by the general officer in charge of mining operations].

INSTITUTION OF ROYAL ENGINEERS. 1922b. *The work of the Royal Engineers in the European War, 1914-19: military mining.* W. & J. Mackay, Chatham, 148pp. [R.E. official account].

MULLINS, L.E. 1965. The mines at Messines. *Royal Engineers Journal,* **79,** 286-292. [Engineer account of the mines].

Selected further reading

PENNYCUICK, J.A.C. 1965. Hill 60 and the mines at Messines. *Royal Engineers Journal*, **79,** 388-397. [Engineer account of the mines].

ROSENBAUM, M.S. 1989. Geological influence on tunnelling under the Western Front at Vimy Ridge. *Proceedings of the Geologists' Association,* **100,** 135-140. [Study of the tunnels under Vimy Ridge]

ROSENBAUM, M.S. & ROSE, E.P.F. 1992. Geology and military tunnels. *Geology Today,* **8,** 92-98. [Authors' experience at Vimy Ridge and in Gibraltar].

TATHAM, H. 1919. Tunnelling in the sand dunes of the Belgian coast. *Transactions of the Institute of Mining and Metallurgy,* **28,** 523-531. [Tunnelling in the dune fields].

WALKER, J.W. 1988. Mining on the Western Front. *Land and Minerals Surveying,* **6,** 523-531. [Reprinted contemporary account].

Geologists at war

MACLEOD, R. 1995. '*Kriegsgeologen* and practical men': military geology and modern memory, 1914-18. *British Journal of the History of Science,* **28,** 427-450. [Discussion of the activities of geologists during the Great War].

ROSE, E.P.F. & ROSENBAUM, M.S. 1993. British military geologists: the formative years to the end of the First World War. *Proceedings of the Geologists' Association,* **104,** 41-50. [Activities of British military geologists].

ROSE, E.P.F. & ROSENBAUM, M.S. 1998. British military geologists through war and peace in the 19th and 20th centuries. In Underhill, J.R. & Guth, P.L. (eds) *Military Geology in War and Peace.* Geological Society of America Reviews in Engineering Geology, Volume XIII, Boulder, Colorado, 29-39. [Activities of British military geologists].

GLOSSARY OF GEOLOGICAL TERMS

ALLUVIUM: - fine sediments transported and deposited by rivers.

ALPINE OROGENY: - Mountain building event during the **Palaeogene** which created the Alpine and Himalayan mountain chains.

ANTICLINE: - folded rock layers, forming a broad symmetrical arch, usually accompanied by a **syncline.**

AXIS (of a fold): - Line of symmetry which divides a fold into two parts or **limbs.**

CHALK: - soft, white limestone composed almost entirely of the skeletons of marine micro-organisms; mostly of **Cretaceous** age in this region. As a formal geological unit, it can be divided into the **Chalk Marl, Middle Chalk** and **Upper Chalk** units.

CHALK MARL: - distinct geological unit comprising layers of chalk and chalky-clay (marl)

CLAY-WITH-FLINTS: - residual clay layer found on top of the **Chalk** which is rich in flints eroded from the softer limestone.

COAL: - Rock type produced by the compaction of vegetable remains.

COAL MEASURES: - Rock units containing seams of **coal.**

DIP: - Angle of inclination of rock units with a horizontal plane.

DRIFT: - term applied to the often loose sediments deposited on the Earth's surface during the **Quaternary.**

DRY VALLEY: - valley containing no surface water usually associated with soluble limestone areas such as chalk; the valleys in northern France were mostly cut during periods of **periglacial** ground freezing (permafrost).

FAULT:- fracture in the Earth's crust which causes displacement of rocks. Faults may be associated with compression, producing thrusts, or extension, producing normal faults.

FAULT SCARP: - steep slope at the Earth's surface initiated by fault - displacement.

FLINT: - a hard, glassy silica rock found in **chalk;** it originates from the solution of organisms with a silica skeleton, the silica often being precipitated in pre-exisiting burrows to produce the characteristically nodular shape.

GLAUCONITE: - a distinctive green mineral commonly found in sandstones, and formed under marine conditions.

HERCYNIAN OROGENY: - Mountain building event during the late **Palaeozoic** which created mountains in Central Europe, including the Ardennes.

ICE AGE: - Period of glacial advance; the last Ice Age, during the **Quaternary** produced massive ice sheets which covered much of Northern Europe.

LOAM: - sediment which contains, in roughly equal proportions, a mixture of sand, silt and clay.

LOESS: - very fine, wind-blown sediments; often formed as dust blown from vegetation-free areas around the front of glaciers and ice sheets.

LIMB (of a fold): - One half of a fold, divided by the **axis.**

Glossary of geological terms

LIMON: - French term referring to a mixture of **loess** and **loam** produced during the Quaternary which is commonly found on top of the **Chalk** in Northern France.

NORMAL FAULT: - fault caused by a phase of extension at the Earth's surface in which one side of the fracture moves downwards under the influence of gravity.

OROGENY/OROGENIC PHASE: - mountain building episode, usually associated with a period of compression caused by plate collision.

PERIGLACIAL: - Frozen ground conditions (permafrost) which produced the frost-shattered surface layer of the **Chalk**; associated with the extensive area to the south the ice sheets produced during the last **Ice Age.**

REGRESSION: - Retreat of the sea from the land during a lowering in sea level.

SYNCLINE: - folded rock layers, forming a broad symmetrical inverted arch, usually accompanied by an **anticline.**

SARSENS: - Residual well-cemented blocks and batches of Palaeogene sand left behind on the surface of the Chalk during erosion; widely used in road building in France.

THRUST: - a fault caused by a compressive phase, which has a low angle fracture plane where the rocks on one side of the fracture ride over those of the other side.

TRANSGRESSION: - Advance of the sea onto the land during periods of rising sea-level.

Geological time scale

GEOLOGICAL TIME SCALE

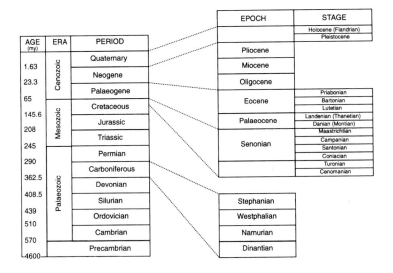

Figure 44. Geological timescale.

And saw a sad land, weak with sweats of dearth,
Gray, cratered like the moon with hollow woe,
And pitted with pocks and scabs of plagues.

Wilfred Owen, *The Show.*